have a few
ks on staff.

Stratus The New Dodge

{The Advanced Peacock}

{The Scorpion}

{The Triangle}

THE NINE PRINCIPAL POSTURES FOR
ACHIEVING GREATER RELAXATION AND SELF-DISCOVERY.

{The Crow}

{The Jeep Grand Cherokee}

{The Half Lotus}

{The Wheel}

{The Bow}

{The Crescent Moon}

JEEP® GRAND CHEROKEE

Any journey of self-discovery starts by finding a quiet place. Inside a Jeep Grand Cherokee Limited, for example. With rich leather-trimmed seats, Automatic Temperature Control and the Jeep Memory System, relaxation is assured. Now picture a secluded location and prepare to unwind. Our exclusive Quadra-Trac® all-the-time four-wheel drive system and available high-output 220 horsepower V8 give you boundless flexibility. Standard dual front air bags† will enhance your growing sense of serenity, as will the rigid side-guard door beams and remote keyless entry system.

To find out more, call 1-800-925-JEEP or visit our Web site at http://www.jeepunpaved.com Jeep ownership. It's a position that's easier than ever to get into.

Jeep®
THERE'S ONLY ONE

†Always wear your seat belt. Jeep is a registered trademark of Chrysler Corporation.

NATIONAL GEOGRAPHIC

FEBRUARY 1997

Departments

Behind the Scenes
Forum
Geographica

Flashback
On Television
Earth Almanac
On Assignment

The Cover

An abandoned Siberian tiger cub named Globus, photographed in Russia, now lives in the Minnesota Zoo. Photograph by Marc Moritsch

♻ Cover printed on recycled-content paper.

For membership please call:
1-800-NGS-LINE
Special device for the hearing-impaired
(TDD) 1-800-548-9797

LINDA BARTLETT

TED CREEDON

All Grown Up, and Staying Put

Vacationing in Ireland last August, staff writer Boris Weintraub ran into Christy Fitzgerald, who as a three-year-old appeared in our April 1976 Dingle Peninsula article. Each summer Christy, now 24, crews for tourists on a Dingle Bay sailboat, where Boris met him. He also works as a mountain guide and teaches Irish dance. He's seen many friends leave Ireland to look for work. "You have to wear a lot of hats if you want to stay," he says.

Write, Now.

SOMETIMES, for professional writers, anything can be preferable to putting words down on paper. Some GEOGRAPHIC staffers pace the floor aimlessly; some stare intently out the window—at nothing in particular. Still others admit to sudden urges to tidy up; somehow, the worst chores are welcome when you're waiting for inspiration.

Assistant Editor Mike Edwards, who has produced 40 stories for the magazine, offers this advice to aspiring writers: "Before you start, paint the living room. Fix the gutters. Clean out the garage. No writer should live in a new house—that denies him essential avoidance maneuvers."

DAVID CLARK

Park and 47th
Attraction.

Park and 61st
Flirtation.

Park and 89th
Conversation.

AL SCHABEN

On the Road Again

"IT'S SURPRISING how ill-prepared some folks are for driving in the desert," says freelance writer Mark Miller, who need not count himself among that number. The California-based author of our *Southwest* driving guide put four months and 16,588 miles on his trusty 1977 Volkswagen Rabbit while writing the book, which follows both the big and back roads of Utah, Arizona, and New Mexico. "I can't tell you how many times I found motorists marooned," he says. "I got so I carried a couple of extra water jugs just for stranded travelers. I handed out more than a dozen. Just another service of your Society."

   Southwest is the third volume in our 12-book *Driving Guides to America* series, which includes both maps and the authors' favorite routes and points of interest in the U.S. and Canada.

JESÚS LÓPEZ

Sounding Good in Mexico

LONGTIME GEOGRAPHIC PHOTOGRAPHER—and now a producer on our Web site, National Geographic Online—Richard Olsenius was used to taking pictures on assignment. But for ten days last summer in Mexico City he captured sounds. Adding "you are there" realism to his Daily Dispatches feature, Richard recorded water splashing in Xochimilco (above), vendors' cries, and mariachi music to supplement written daily reports. "The new Web technology is kind of a toy now," he says, "but not for long."

Their Life in Lichens

IT'S NOT THAT Stephen and Sylvia Sharnoff are obsessed with lichens. But the California husband-and-wife photographic team (below), producers of our lichens story, are well into their third decade of photographing and gathering some 5,000 specimens. Sponsored by the Missouri Botanical Garden, they are working with lichenologist Irwin Brodo of the Canadian Museum of Nature to compile *Lichens of North America*, a

DAVID SHARNOFF

definitive, color-illustrated manual that will be published by Yale University Press.

   In the past seven years of lichen hunting, the Sharnoffs have traveled nearly 100,000 miles in a small recreational vehicle. And yes, sometimes while watching TV, they do exhibit as much interest in the rocks in the scenery as in the plot. But they are really not all that obsessed. "We also have a great interest," Sylvia reports, "in slime molds."
                              —MAGGIE ZACKOWITZ

■ FOR INFORMATION

Call: 1-800-NGS-LINE
  (1-800-647-5463)
  Toll free from U.S., Canada
  8 a.m.–8 p.m. ET, Mon.–Fri.
  Special device for the hearing-impaired (TDD) 1-800-548-9797
Write: National Geographic Society
  1145 17th Street N.W.
  Washington, D.C. 20036-4688
Online:
  World Wide Web:
  http://www.nationalgeographic.com
  CompuServe: GO NATIONAL GEOGRAPHIC

There are few places in this world where you can feel so much in one afternoon.

Welcome to Park Avenue.

The orchestral acoustics, supple leather seating and all the subtle pleasures and conveniences confirm it: there is no more intimate place on Park Avenue than in Park Avenue.

PARK AVENUE BY BUICK

THE POWER OF UNDERSTATEMENT

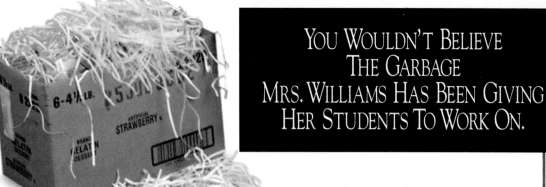

YOU WOULDN'T BELIEVE THE GARBAGE MRS. WILLIAMS HAS BEEN GIVING HER STUDENTS TO WORK ON.

When Beverly Ann Williams noticed all the paper and expensive art supplies that wound up in the trash at the end of her classes, she found a very artistic solution to the problem. Now, instead of throwing art supplies in the trash, she uses the trash itself as art supplies. Having her students recycle the shredded paper, cups and other styrofoam products into surprisingly creative works of art.

For letting her eighth grade students see just how beautiful recycling can be, State Farm is pleased to present our Good Neighbor Award to Beverly Ann Williams, along with $5,000 for the Union Academy Magnet Middle School of Bartow, Florida.

Forum

In the October 1996 issue "U.S. National Wildlife Refuges" drew a large and positive response, but the fact that hunting is sometimes allowed caused such reactions as: "Perhaps the name 'killing field' would be more fitting than 'wildlife sanctuary.'" Readers of our Morocco article caught us in a time warp about the length of Jimi Hendrix's sojourn in that country.

National Wildlife Refuges

Americans owe an immense debt of gratitude to leaders such as Theodore Roosevelt and visionaries like John Muir. We are the beneficiaries of their wisdom. With farmlands, wildlife habitat, and open lands being lost to development at a record rate, our irreplaceable public lands become more precious with each passing day. We cannot allow them to be sold or exploited for short-term profits. A commitment to future generations, not short-sighted greed, must be the principle guiding our public lands policies.

WILLIAM H. MURPHY
St. Johns, Michigan

Regardless of the wise use of federal lands for nature protection, conservation through private action remains the key to success in these efforts. The Nature Conservancy, which acquires lands that become part of national wildlife refuges and maintains adjacent protected areas, should have been a part of your story. This nonconfrontational organization of nearly one million has pinpointed more than 9.3 million acres in the United States for protection; see "Quietly Conserving Nature" in your December 1988 issue.

RICHARD A. CARPENTER
Charlottesville, Virginia

Webster's definition for refuge is (1) shelter or protection from danger or distress (2) a place that provides shelter or protection. How are national wildlife refuge lands a "refuge" for wildlife when we allow hunting, fishing, planes, roads, boating, oil drilling, unethical trapping, and recreation to go on in these areas? Improvement for refuges does not start with legislation allowing even more distress.

RITA SCOTT
Chesapeake, Virginia

When you state that federal refuges are founded on the principle of putting wildlife first, am I, a 45-year member of the Society, to assume that wildlife comes before humankind? The pendulum has swung too far.

EARL MacDOUGALL
North Bay, Ontario

Your excellent article was marred by several swipes at military aircraft training. Aircraft noise and sonic booms are no more intense than natural thunder. In California one of the largest colonies of the endangered least tern has grown up between the 75-decibel runways of Alameda Naval Air Station. The Defense Department has an agreement with the Nature Conservancy to advise the military's natural resource managers on protecting biosystems on its installations and training ranges. The Air Force and Navy have adjusted flight training schedules to accommodate bird migration routes as well as breeding seasons for sensitive species such as bighorn sheep. Beyond this, there is simply no scientific evidence that aircraft training adversely affects wildlife. The tow target (page 31) had less impact on habitat than the feet of the thousands of nature lovers, like your photographer and your author, who hike through those areas.

RAYMOND SWENSON
Lt. Colonel, USAF (Ret.)
Sandy, Utah

Federal Lands Map

Thank you for including the North Country National Scenic Trail. For 15 years we have been trying to raise awareness of this trail. We have just exceeded 1,300 miles of marked and maintained trail, certified by the National Park Service, with another 600 miles completed but not yet certified.

DEREK BLOUNT, *President*
North Country Trail Association
Grand Rapids, Michigan

Solid green and yellow blocks to identify Forest Service and Bureau of Land Management holdings do not convey the checkerboard pattern of land ownership so common in the West. Private forest and ranchlands, often in alternating square-mile blocks, adjacent to federal land have shattered the ecological integrity of many areas.

BLAKE PANTON
Seattle, Washington

I was disappointed that U.S. Army Corps of Engineers lands were not included. The Corps owns and manages 11.7 million acres of land and water throughout the U.S. In addition to flood control, Corps projects provide areas for recreation and habitat for wildlife. Many contain threatened and endangered species, sensitive lands, and archaeological sites.

TERESA J. RASMUSSEN
Lawrence, Kansas

Located a hundred miles off Texas and Louisiana in the Gulf of Mexico, the Flower Garden Banks National Marine Sanctuary, though not depicted, is a wilderness visited by thousands of divers every year. Its natural inhabitants include species that people travel worldwide to see: manta rays, sea turtles, whale sharks, and schooling hammerheads — all in one place. Great map otherwise!

STEPHEN GITTINGS, *Manager*
Flower Garden Banks NMS
Bryan, Texas

WILL YOU turn the corner?

Or keep heading down the same road?

Will you go the next mile?

Or be content

to travel

in the same circles?

Today,

technology is pressing on.

Aren't you just a little curious

what's over the next hill?

The 1997 Chrysler Concorde LXi

CAB-FORWARD DESIGN, 3.5 LITER 24-VALVE V6, DRIVER-ADAPTIVE TRANSMISSION, SPEED-SENSITIVE STEERING, INDEPENDENT TOURING SUSPENSI

What's new in your world?

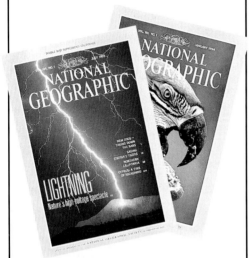

African Gold

I was delighted to see the cover of the October edition highlighting an article on the Asante people and their "African Gold." My pleasure diminished when all I found were eight pages of beautiful color photographs supported by amplified headings. The Asante people are one of the world's great nations, with a proud history that has influenced many other nations. They remain a major force in African development, and through their dispersal to America and Europe they make enormous contributions to their host nations.

REV. ANTHONY BRAZIER
High Wycombe, England

Kuril Islands

The article ignores the sacrifice made in the Kurils by many of my comrades-in-arms in the final years of World War II. After the Japanese were driven from westernmost Alaska (the Aleutian Islands) in 1943, plans went on to forge an Aleutian-Kuril "bridge to victory." Under the cover of dirty weather, U.S. submarines, destroyers, and aircraft based in Alaska launched the earliest attacks on the Japanese homeland, except for the Doolittle raid. Many planes were shot down over the Kurils, which were later seized by Soviet troops.

LOREN McINTYRE
Arlington, Virginia

China's Terra-cotta Warriors

Louis Mazzatenta's article gives a fascinating update on the painstaking archaeological work going on in Xian. Might it be possible that the terra-cotta army of Qin Shi Huang is not only evidence of the emperor's quest for immortality and eternal power but also a life-size record of those who served in battle with honor and dignity? What a brilliant way to instill pride and loyalty in the rank and file.

R. PETER SAUNDERS
Bellevue, Washington

In a photograph on page 76 a technician "injects glue made of shark's lung" under paint. I was under the impression that sharks were equipped with gills, not lungs. Was this an error of translation, or are sharks in China anatomically different from those elsewhere?

RICHARD ELLIS
New York, New York

Good catch. The translation should have been "fish parts."

Morocco

The article was interesting and objective. However, as an Algerian woman, I felt insulted by the Moroccan's quote on pages 123-4. We Algerians have an identity and roots too. Likewise, we have never been obsessed with religion. Our search for democracy stumbles at many problems linked to a weak economy, and we are paying the price. Algerians nevertheless keep their dignity and respect and

proved it in 1996 when they massively voted under the fundamentalist threat. There is a minority of fundamentalists trying to create chaos, but this shouldn't be the opportunity for our neighbors to try to emerge as "different."

BACHIRA SALHI-PASSOT
Nice, France

I was surprised to read that Morocco is of "small size" since it is larger in area than Texas and twice the size of Germany. In population it is larger than any U.S. state, except California.

DAVID MISHAN
Houston, Texas

The article was well-documented and well thought out. The writer, whose sense of humor added to the beauty of the article, avoided the us/them dichotomy that often turns non-Westerners into exotic creatures who are helpless in dealing with modern times. The Moroccan is hardworking, devout, practical, and very tolerant. The fact that Benguerir's billboard boasts that it is the city of the future, though it made me smile, is meaningful. It tells much about the optimism and perseverance of the Moroccan people, who believe in a better future.

MOULAY ALI BOUANANI
Toledo, Ohio

For a country with a long history, very little thought is given to the future. Therefore, treating a customer or business partner fairly is of little concern; grab the quick profit and the client be damned. When one isn't being hustled, one is struck by the poverty and stark contrast between the classes. The black market and drug trade would appear to make up the lion's share of the economy.

EDWIN NELSON
Casablanca, Morocco

Jimi Hendrix did not spend five years in Diabat. He visited Morocco only once — in the summer of 1969 on holiday. In addition, sand was an often used metaphor in his songwriting, but there is no documentation to support the claim that he wrote "Castles Made of [not 'in the'] Sand" after spending time in Morocco. The song was written in 1967.

BYRON GORDON
San Francisco, California

Letters for FORUM should be sent to National Geographic Magazine, Box 37448, Washington, D.C. 20013-7448, or by fax to 202-828-5460, or via the Internet to ngsforum@ nationalgeographic.com. Include name, address, and daytime telephone. Letters may be edited for clarity and space.

NATIONAL GEOGRAPHIC ONLINE

Features, maps, questions, contests. Join the rest of the Geographic family in an electronic adventure. Shop at the NGS Store. Visit our World Wide Web site at *http://www.nationalgeographic.com* or GO NATIONAL GEOGRAPHIC through CompuServe.

CATERA™

For the authorized Catera dealer nearest you,
call 1-800-333-4CAD or visit us at www.catera.com.

THE CADDY THAT ZIGS.™

STARTING AT $29,995*

 CADILLAC.

Photo: Bruce Bennett ©1996

The most important job of your life just might be your first.

As a member of Teach For America, you will be part of the national teacher corps of outstanding recent college graduates from diverse cultural backgrounds who commit two years to teach in America's under-resourced urban and rural public schools.

You don't have to be an education major. Teach For America is seeking talented, dedicated individuals from every academic major who want to ensure that all children in this nation have the opportunity to attain an excellent education. There is a particular need for people of color, bilingual speakers, and math, science, and foreign language majors.

To get information and an application before the deadline, call us, reach us online, or contact your career placement adviser on campus.

This is your chance to become part of the nationwide movement of dynamic individuals who have joined Teach For America and assumed leadership roles in classrooms and schools across the country. Your decision will affect not only the rest of your life but the lives of many others.

1-800-832-1230
http://www.teachforamerica.org

TEACHFORAMERICA
AN AMERICORPS PROGRAM

esc to a whole new world.

A SIMPLE YET ACCU
OF HOW OUR ANTI-

Finally, there's a CAR PROTECTION device whose bite is worse than its bark. Ford Motor Company engineers have developed what's being hailed as one of the most powerful ANTI-THEFT inventions ever. A remarkable computer chip that's embedded in the key. This chip sends a distinct ELECTRONIC SIGNAL directly to the car's engine before it will ever start. You see, at FORD MOTOR COMPANY, we're not only committed to building the best

Available on select Ford, Lincoln and Mercury products. For more information, contact us on the Internet at: http://www.ford.com

RATE DEMONSTRATION
THEFT KEY WORKS.

quality cars and trucks in the WORLD but also to making absolutely sure our CUSTOMERS

keep them. Because we believe your car should always be there for you. Like a best friend.

· FORD · FORD TRUCKS ·  · LINCOLN · MERCURY ·

QUALITY IS JOB 1

FLORIDA MUSEUM OF NATURAL HISTORY (ABOVE AND ABOVE LEFT)

Colonial Florida Fort Recalls
a Shining Moment in Black History

HIDDEN IN THE SALT MARSHES of northern St. Augustine, Florida, the frontier outpost of Fort Mose might be forgotten today except for one startling fact: It was the first free black colonial town in what is now the United States. Its residents, African slaves from British plantations to the north, had found refuge by escaping to Spanish-held Florida—and converting to Catholicism.

Declared a national historic landmark in 1994, Fort Mose was brought back to life after a search of Spanish documents by historian Jane Landers, now at Vanderbilt University, and two years of excavations led by archaeologist Kathleen Deagan (above).

Her team, with assistance from black Florida legislators such as former State Representative Bill Clark, at far left, uncovered everyday items used for cooking, clothing, shelter, and defense. It also found a handcrafted silver medal (above, left) with an image of St. Christopher on one side and a sailor's compass rose on the other. Many escaped slaves served as crewmen on Spanish ships.

At a time when both England and Spain claimed northern Florida (map), "slaves in the Carolinas knew of the possibility of freedom in Spanish Florida," says Landers. In 1738 the Spanish formed a freedmen's militia and moved one hundred black men, women, and children from St. Augustine to build the 65-foot-square Fort Mose. Two years later a British attack forced the residents to flee to St. Augustine. After 1752, blacks returned to a new, larger Fort Mose nearby, shown in this infrared image (left). In 1763 Florida was ceded to England, and the Spanish blacks moved to Cuba.

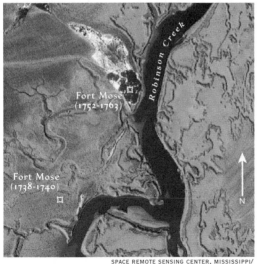

SPACE REMOTE SENSING CENTER, MISSISSIPPI/
FLORIDA MUSEUM OF NATURAL HISTORY

Now You Can Afford To Be Choosy.

Mercury Sable Wagon

Mercury Sable Sedan

CHOOSE EITHER A ROOMY SEDAN OR STYLISH WAGON FOR THE SAME PRICE.

Choosing between a sedan or wagon used to be so simple. You'd choose the sedan if you wanted style. The wagon if you wanted more room. That is, until Mercury came up with the stylish Sable Wagon and the roomy Sable Sedan. So, to make the choice a little easier, we gave both innovative shapes the same affordable figure. Your choice of a comparably equipped sedan or wagon. Same price. With premium touches like triple door seals for a quiet ride. And the ability to go 100,000 miles before the first scheduled tune-up.* Sable Sedan. Or Sable Wagon. Either way, you can't go wrong. To figure out which shape is right for you, call 1 800 446-8888 for a free brochure.

Mercury
IMAGINE YOURSELF
IN A MERCURY

www.mercuryvehicles.com

*Under normal driving conditions with routine fluid/filter changes.

"You don't need four degrees to understand how easy it is to save with the Ford Citibank Card."

David Joyce
B.A., M. Divinity,
M.S., Ed.D.
Saved $1,040

David Joyce calls it the Ph.D. of credit cards. Because every time he uses the Ford Citibank Card, he gets 5% back. So can you. And that can add up to a huge money-saving Ford Rebate* toward the purchase or Red Carpet Lease of any new Ford, Lincoln, or Mercury. So make your best deal an even better one. It's the smart thing to do. Call **1-800-374-7777** for the Ford Citibank Card.

The No-Annual-Fee Ford Citibank Card.

It's just too good to pass up.

DAVID DOUBILET

The Sudden Decline of the Spotted Handfish

A SLOW-MOVING, shallow-water creature, the spotted handfish (above) rarely swims. Instead, like other handfish, it "walks" along the seafloor on its fins. But this species may be walking toward extinction: It is the first marine fish listed under Australia's Endangered Species Act.

The eight species of handfish take their name from armlike side fins with extremities resembling human hands. In the early 1980s the spotted handfish, which can reach five inches in length, was abundant off southeast Tasmania. A 1982 guide to Tasmanian fishes called it the handfish species most commonly encountered by divers. Now, says marine biologist Barry Bruce, it's rare: Recent surveys of its home waters in the Derwent estuary and adjoining bays turned up only three dozen.

No one is sure what caused the decline, but experts suggest siltation of the estuary, urban effluent, or predation by a new neighbor, the northern Pacific sea star, which probably arrived in the ballast of ships during the 1980s.

Sea Tragedy Eggs On Life Raft Inventor

EGGS ARE DESIGNED by nature to protect what's inside, reasoned Canadian inventor Vincent Thériault. That's why, after 15 years of tinkering to design a better life raft, he devised one that looks like an egg (below).

"The shape has shock resistance," he says. If a wave smacks the raft against something, the impact is deflected, claims Thériault.

A former sailor, Thériault began his efforts after an oil platform sank off the Newfoundland coast, killing 84 workers. More than 25 fishing boats around his home in Caraquet, New Brunswick, now carry the ten-foot-long fireresistant fiberglass life raft, which seats six, provides air through two ceiling vents, and is dubbed Esperanto for the artificial international language.

GILLES DAIGLE

JOYCE POOLE, ELEPHANT PHOTO LIBRARY

What Caused an Elephant's Death?

DURING HIS 45 YEARS OF LIFE, Beach Ball was an object of scientific study, a film star, and a beloved playmate of children in his home, Kenya's Amboseli National Park. When his body was found near park headquarters in August, there was blood on his trunk, but no autopsy was performed to determine the cause of his death. Some elephant experts, noting that he was seen in robust health the night before, believe poachers may have killed him as they have other bulls in Kenya and Tanzania (GEOGRAPHIC, July 1995). Officials of the Kenya Wildlife Service insist he died of natural causes, saying only three elephants were poached in 1996. "It's a death that will continue to confuse us," says Christie Feral of the Washington-based African Wildlife Foundation.

Beach Ball was named by researcher Joyce Poole, who monitored his behavior for 14 years. "Everything about him was round," she explained in the National Geographic EXPLORER film "Coming of Age With Elephants." He also was featured in two BBC films by Poole's mentor, Cynthia Moss.

—BORIS WEINTRAUB

IF YOU THINK YOU
HAVE TOENAIL FUNGUS,
ASK YOUR DOCTOR
OR OTHER HEALTHCARE
PROFESSIONAL, OR CALL

1-800-595-NAILS ext. 253

AND GET YOUR
FREE SPORANOX "KICK-IT KIT."

TOENAIL WITH FUNGUS.

100 mg

sporanox®

(itraconazole capsules)

Before prescribing, please consult complete prescribing information of which the following is a brief summary.

WARNING: Coadministration of terfenadine with itraconazole is contraindicated. Serious cardiovascular adverse events, including death, ventricular tachycardia, and torsades de pointes have occurred in patients taking itraconazole concomitantly with terfenadine. This is due to elevated terfenadine concentrations caused by itraconazole. See CONTRAINDICATIONS, WARNINGS, and PRECAUTIONS sections.

Another oral azole antifungal, ketoconazole, inhibits the metabolism of astemizole, resulting in elevated plasma concentrations of astemizole and its active metabolite desmethylastemizole, which may prolong QT intervals. Based on results of an *in vitro* study and the chemical resemblance of itraconazole and ketoconazole, coadministration of astemizole and itraconazole is contraindicated. See CONTRAINDICATIONS, WARNINGS, and PRECAUTIONS sections.

Coadministration of cisapride with itraconazole is contraindicated. Serious cardiovascular adverse events including death, ventricular tachycardia, and torsades de pointes have occurred in patients taking itraconazole concomitantly with cisapride. See CONTRAINDICATIONS, WARNINGS, and PRECAUTIONS sections.

INDICATIONS AND USAGE

SPORANOX (itraconazole capsules) is indicated for the treatment of the following fungal infections in immunocompromised and non-immunocompromised patients:

1. Blastomycosis, pulmonary and extrapulmonary;
2. Histoplasmosis, including chronic cavitary pulmonary disease and disseminated, non-meningeal histoplasmosis;
3. Aspergillosis, pulmonary and extrapulmonary, in patients who are intolerant of or who are refractory to amphotericin B therapy; and
4. Onychomycosis due to dermatophytes (tinea unguium) of the toenail with or without fingernail involvement.

CONTRAINDICATIONS

Coadministration of terfenadine, astemizole or cisapride with SPORANOX (itraconazole capsules) is contraindicated. (See BOX WARNING, WARNINGS, and PRECAUTIONS sections.)

Concomitant administration of SPORANOX with oral triazolam or with oral midazolam is contraindicated. (See PRECAUTIONS section.)

SPORANOX should not be administered for the treatment of onychomycosis to pregnant patients or to women contemplating pregnancy.

SPORANOX is contraindicated in patients who have shown hypersensitivity to the drug or its excipients. There is no information regarding cross hypersensitivity between itraconazole and other azole antifungal agents. Caution should be used in prescribing SPORANOX to patients with hypersensitivity to other azoles.

WARNINGS

In U.S. clinical trials prior to marketing, there have been three cases of reversible idiosyncratic hepatitis reported among more than 2500 patients taking SPORANOX (itraconazole capsules). One patient outside the U.S. developed fulminant hepatitis and died during SPORANOX administration. Since this patient was on multiple medications, the causal association with SPORANOX is uncertain. If clinical signs and symptoms consistent with liver disease develop that may be attributable to itraconazole, SPORANOX should be discontinued.

Prior to U.S. marketing, there have been three cases of life-threatening cardiac dysrhythmias and one death reported in patients receiving terfenadine and itraconazole. (See BOX WARNING, CONTRAINDICATIONS, and PRECAUTIONS sections.)

Coadministration of astemizole with SPORANOX is contraindicated. (See BOX WARNING, CONTRAINDICATIONS, and PRECAUTIONS sections.)

Concomitant administration of oral ketoconazole with cisapride has resulted in markedly elevated cisapride plasma concentrations, prolonged QT intervals, and has rarely been associated with ventricular arrhythmias and torsades de pointes. Due to potent *in vitro* inhibition of the hepatic enzyme system mainly responsible for the metabolism of cisapride (cytochrome P450 3A4), itraconazole is also expected to markedly raise cisapride plasma concentrations; therefore, concomitant use of cisapride with SPORANOX is contraindicated. (See BOX WARNING, CONTRAINDICATIONS, and PRECAUTIONS sections.)

PRECAUTIONS

General: Hepatic enzyme test values should be monitored in patients with preexisting hepatic function abnormalities. Hepatic enzyme test values should be monitored periodically in all patients receiving continuous treatment for more than one month or at any time a patient develops signs or symptoms suggestive of liver dysfunction.

SPORANOX (itraconazole capsules) should be administered after a full meal.

Under fasted conditions, itraconazole absorption was decreased in the presence of decreased gastric acidity. The absorption of itraconazole may be decreased with the concomitant administration of antacids or gastric acid secretion suppressors. Studies conducted under fasted conditions demonstrated that administration with 8 ounces of a cola beverage resulted in increased absorption of itraconazole in AIDS patients with relative or absolute achlorhydria. This increase relative to the effects of a full meal is unknown.

Information for patients: Patients should be instructed to take SPORANOX with a full meal.

Patients should be instructed to report any signs and symptoms that may suggest liver dysfunction so that the appropriate laboratory testing can be done. Such signs and symptoms may include unusual fatigue, anorexia, nausea and/or vomiting, jaundice, dark urine or pale stool.

Drug interactions: Both itraconazole and its major metabolite, hydroxyitraconazole, are inhibitors of the cytochrome P450 3A4 enzyme system. Coadministration of SPORANOX and drugs primarily metabolized by the cytochrome P450 3A4 enzyme system may result in increased plasma concentrations of the drugs that could increase or prolong both therapeutic and adverse effects. Therefore, unless otherwise specified, appropriate dosage adjustments may be necessary.

Coadministration of terfenadine with SPORANOX has led to elevated plasma concentrations of terfenadine, resulting in rare instances of life-threatening cardiac dysrhythmias and one death. (See BOX WARNING, CONTRAINDICATIONS, and WARNINGS sections.)

Another oral azole antifungal, ketoconazole, inhibits the metabolism of astemizole, resulting in elevated plasma concentrations of astemizole and its active metabolite desmethylastemizole which may prolong QT intervals. *In vitro* data suggest that itraconazole, when compared to ketoconazole, has a less pronounced effect on the biotransformation system responsible for the metabolism of astemizole. Based on the chemical resemblance of itraconazole and ketoconazole, coadministration of astemizole with itraconazole is contraindicated. (See BOX WARNING, CONTRAINDICATIONS, and WARNINGS sections.)

Human pharmacokinetics data indicate that oral ketoconazole potently inhibits the metabolism of cisapride resulting in an eight-fold increase in the mean AUC of cisapride. Data suggest that coadministration of oral ketoconazole and cisapride can result in prolongation of the QT interval on the ECG. *In vitro* data suggest that itraconazole also markedly inhibits the biotransformation system mainly responsible for the metabolism of cisapride; therefore concomitant administration of SPORANOX with cisapride is contraindicated. (See BOX WARNING, CONTRAINDICATIONS, and WARNINGS sections.)

Coadministration of SPORANOX with oral midazolam or triazolam has resulted in elevated plasma concentrations of the latter two drugs. This may potentiate and prolong hypnotic and sedative effects. These agents should not be used in patients treated with SPORANOX. If midazolam is administered parenterally, special precaution is required since the sedative effect may be prolonged. (See CONTRAINDICATIONS section.)

Coadministration of SPORANOX and cyclosporine, tacrolimus or digoxin has led to increased plasma concentrations of the latter three drugs. Cyclosporine, tacrolimus and digoxin concentrations should be monitored at the initiation of SPORANOX therapy and frequently thereafter, and the dose of these three drug products adjusted appropriately.

There have been rare reports of rhabdomyolysis involving renal transplant patients receiving the combination of SPORANOX, cyclosporine, and the HMG-CoA reductase inhibitors lovastatin or simvastatin. Rhabdomyolysis has been observed in patients receiving HMG-CoA reductase inhibitors administered alone (at recommended dosages) or concomitantly with immunosuppressive drugs including cyclosporine.

When SPORANOX was coadministered with phenytoin, rifampin, or H_2 antagonists, reduced plasma concentrations of itraconazole were reported. The physician is advised to monitor the plasma concentrations of itraconazole when any of these drugs is taken concurrently, and to increase the dose of SPORANOX if necessary. Although no studies have been conducted, concomitant administration of SPORANOX and phenytoin may alter the metabolism of phenytoin; therefore, plasma concentrations of phenytoin should also be monitored when it is given concurrently with SPORANOX.

It has been reported that SPORANOX enhances the anticoagulant effect of coumarin-like drugs. Therefore, prothrombin time should be carefully monitored in patients receiving SPORANOX and coumarin-like drugs simultaneously.

Plasma concentrations of azole antifungal agents are reduced when given concurrently with isoniazid. Itraconazole plasma concentrations should be monitored when SPORANOX and isoniazid are coadministered.

Severe hypoglycemia has been reported in patients concomitantly receiving azole antifungal agents and oral hypoglycemic agents. Blood glucose concentrations should be carefully monitored when SPORANOX and oral hypoglycemic agents are coadministered.

Tinnitus and decreased hearing have been reported in patients concomitantly receiving SPORANOX and quinidine. Edema has been reported in patients concomitantly receiving SPORANOX and dihydropyridine calcium channel blockers. Appropriate dosage adjustments may be necessary.

The results from a study in which eight HIV-infected individuals were treated with zidovudine, 8 ± 0.4 mg/kg/day, showed that the pharmacokinetics of zidovudine were not affected during concomitant administration of SPORANOX, 100 mg b.i.d.

Carcinogenesis, Mutagenesis and Impairment of Fertility: Itraconazole showed no evidence of carcinogenicity potential in mice treated orally for 23 months at dosage levels up to 80 mg/kg/day [approximately 10x the maximum recommended human dose (MRHD)]. Male rats treated with 25 mg/kg/day (3.1x MRHD) had a slightly increased incidence of soft tissue sarcoma. These sarcomas may have been a consequence of hypercholesterolemia, which is a response of rats, but not dogs or humans, to chronic itraconazole administration. Female rats treated with 50 mg/kg/day (6.25x MRHD) had an increased incidence of squamous cell carcinoma of the lung (2/50) as compared to the untreated group. Although the occurrence of squamous cell carcinoma in the lung is extremely uncommon in untreated rats, the increase in this study was not statistically significant.

Itraconazole produced no mutagenic effects when assayed in appropriate bacterial, non-mammalian and mammalian test systems.

Itraconazole did not affect the fertility of male or female rats treated orally with dosage levels of up to 40 mg/kg/day (5x MRHD) even though parental toxicity was present at this dosage level. More severe signs of parental toxicity, including death, were present in the next higher dosage level, 160 mg/kg/day (20x MRHD).

Pregnancy: Teratogenic Effects. Pregnancy Category C: Itraconazole was found to cause a dose-related increase in maternal toxicity, embryotoxicity and teratogenicity in rats at dosage levels of approximately 40-160 mg/kg/day (5-20x MRHD) and in mice at dosage levels of approximately 80 mg/kg/day (10x MRHD). In rats, the teratogenicity consisted of major skeletal defects; in mice it consisted of encephaloceles and/or macroglossia.

There are no studies in pregnant women. SPORANOX should be used for the treatment of systemic fungal infections in pregnancy only if the benefit outweighs the potential risk. SPORANOX should not be administered for the treatment of onychomycosis to pregnant patients or to women contemplating pregnancy. SPORANOX should not be administered to women of child-bearing potential for the treatment of onychomycosis unless they are taking effective measures to prevent pregnancy and the patient begins therapy on the second or third day of the next normal menstrual period. Effective contraception should be continued throughout SPORANOX therapy and for 2 months following treatment.

Nursing Mothers: Itraconazole is excreted in human milk; therefore, SPORANOX should not be administered to nursing women.

Pediatric Use: The efficacy and safety of SPORANOX have not been established in pediatric patients. No pharmacokinetic data are available in children. A small number of patients age 3 to 16 years have been treated with 100 mg/day of itraconazole for systemic fungal infections and no serious unexpected adverse effects have been reported.

In three toxicology studies using rats, itraconazole induced bone defects at dosage levels as low as 20 mg/kg/day (2.5x MRHD). The induced defects included reduced bone plate activity, thinning of the zona compacta of the large bones and increased bone fragility. At a dosage level of 80 mg/kg/day (10x MRHD) over one year or 160 mg/kg/day (20x MRHD) for six months, itraconazole induced small tooth pulp with hypocellular appearance in some rats.

While no such bone toxicity has been reported in adult patients, the long term effect of itraconazole in pediatric patients is unknown.

HIV-infected Patients: Because hypochlorhydria has been reported in HIV-infected individuals, the absorption of itraconazole in these patients may be decreased.

The results from a study in which eight HIV-infected individuals were treated with zidovudine, 8 ± 0.4 mg/kg/day, showed that the pharmacokinetics of zidovudine were not affected during concomitant administration of SPORANOX, 100 mg b.i.d.

ADVERSE REACTIONS

In U.S. clinical trials prior to marketing, there have been three cases of reversible idiosyncratic hepatitis reported among more than 2500 patients. One patient outside the U.S. developed fulminant hepatitis and died during SPORANOX (itraconazole capsules) administration. Because this patient was on multiple medications, the causal association with SPORANOX is uncertain. (See WARNINGS section.)

ONYCHOMYCOSIS:

Adverse events in the following table led to either temporary or permanent discontinuation of treatment:

Body System/Adverse Event	Incidence (%) (n=112)
Elevated Liver Enzymes (>2x normal range)	4%
Gastrointestinal Disorders	4%
Rash	3%
Hypertension	2%
Orthostatic Hypotension	1%
Headache	1%
Malaise	1%
Myalgia	1%
Vasculitis	1%
Vertigo	1%

SYSTEMIC FUNGAL INFECTIONS:

Adverse experience data in the following table are derived from 602 patients treated for systemic fungal disease in U.S. clinical trials, who were immunocompromised or receiving multiple concomitant medications. Of these patients, treatment was discontinued in 10.5% of patients due to adverse events. The median duration before discontinuation of therapy was 81 days, with a range of 2-776 days. The table lists adverse events reported by at least 1% of patients.

Body System/Adverse Event (Incidence ≥ 1%)	Incidence (%)
Gastrointestinal Disorders	
Nausea	10.6
Vomiting	5.1
Diarrhea	3.3
Abdominal Pain	1.5
Anorexia	1.2
Body as a Whole	
Edema	3.5
Fatigue	2.8
Fever	2.5
Malaise	1.2
Skin and Appendages	
Rash	8.6*
Pruritus	2.5
Central and Peripheral Nervous System	
Headache	3.8
Dizziness	1.7
Psychiatric Disorders	
Libido decreased	1.2
Somnolence	1.2
Cardiovascular Disorders	
Hypertension	3.2
Metabolic and Nutritional Disorders	
Hypokalemia	2.0
Urinary System Disorders	
Albuminuria	1.2
Liver and Biliary System Disorders	
Hepatic function abnormal	2.7
Reproductive Disorders, Male	
Impotence	1.2

*Rash tends to occur more frequently in immunocompromised patients receiving immunosuppressive medications.

Adverse events infrequently reported in all studies included: constipation, gastritis, depression, insomnia, tinnitus, menstrual disorder, adrenal insufficiency, gynecomastia and male breast pain.

In worldwide postmarketing experience with SPORANOX, allergic reactions including rash, pruritus, urticaria, angioedema and in rare instances, anaphylaxis and Stevens-Johnson syndrome, have been reported. Marketing experiences have also included reports of elevated liver enzymes and rare hepatitis. Although the causal association with SPORANOX is uncertain, rare hypertriglyceridemia and isolated cases of neuropathy have also been reported.

OVERDOSAGE

Itraconazole is not removed by dialysis. In the event of accidental overdosage, supportive measures, including gastric lavage with sodium bicarbonate, should be employed.

No significant lethality was observed when itraconazole was administered orally to mice and rats at dosage levels of 320 mg/kg or to dogs at 200 mg/kg.

Rev. April 1995, September 1995

world leader in antifungal research

JANSSEN · PHARMACEUTICA · RESEARCH FOUNDATION ·

Titusville, NJ 08560-0200

IN PRIMITIVE TIMES,
IT WOULD'VE BEEN A GOD.

It has the qualities man has revered and respected for thousands of years. The power to tame the forces of nature. The prowess to navigate almost any terrain. The Toyota Land Cruiser. In its 40-year reign in the United States it has become the paradigm of off-road authenticity, offering full-time 4WD, dual air bags, ABS and an interior so roomy, it can inspire awe in up to seven adults at once. Land Cruiser. For us mortals, it's the ultimate.

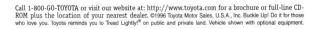

TOYOTA LAND CRUISER
I love what you do for me

NATIONAL GEOGRAPHIC MAGAZINE

WILLIAM L. ALLEN, *Editor*

Associate Editors

ELIZABETH A. MOIZE, ROBERT M. POOLE

SENIOR ASSISTANT EDITORS

ROBERT BOOTH, *Production* • ALLEN CARROLL, *Cartography*
WILLIAM T. DOUTHITT, *Special Projects* • RICK GORE, *Science* • DAVID JEFFERY, *Legends*
THOMAS R. KENNEDY, *Photography* • PETER MILLER, *Expeditions*
JOHN G. MITCHELL, *Environment* • OLIVER PAYNE, *Manuscripts*
CONSTANCE H. PHELPS, *Layout and Design* • LESLEY B. ROGERS, *Research*
W. ALLAN ROYCE, *Illustrations* • CHRISTOPHER P. SLOAN, *Art* • GEORGE E. STUART, *Archaeology*

EDITORIAL

Assistant Editors: Don Belt, Judith Brown, Mike Edwards, Alice J. Hall, Jane Vessels. Bernard Ohanian, *Japanese Edition*. **Senior Writers:** John L. Eliot, Cathy Newman, Joel L. Swerdlow, Priit J. Vesilind. **Senior Editorial Staff:** Larry Kohl, Carol B. Lutyk, Thomas O'Neill, Peter L. Porteous, Jennifer Reek, Cliff Tarpy, Meg Nottingham Walsh, Boris Weintraub, A. R. Williams. **Production:** John L. McIntosh. **Editorial Staff:** Cassandra Franklin-Barbajosa, Lisa Moore LaRoe, Alan Mairson, William R. Newcott, Glenn Oeland, Katherine Ozment, Margaret G. Zackowitz. **Research:** Michaeline A. Sweeney, *Assoc. Director; Senior Researchers:* Carolyn H. Anderson, Judith F. Bell, Kathy B. Maher, Barbara W. McConnell, Jeanne E. Peters, Abigail A. Tipton. *Researchers:* Eva P. Dasher, Alice J. Dunn, Christopher Scaptura, Robin Tunnicliff. *Legends:* Victoria C. Ducheneaux. *Planning Council:* Mary McPeak, David W. Wooddell

ILLUSTRATIONS

Photography: Kent J. Kobersteen, *Assoc. Director;* Susan A. Smith, *Asst. Dir.;* Sam Abell, William Albert Allard, Sisse Brimberg, Jodi Cobb, Chris Johns, Michael Nichols. **Illustrations Editors:** Dennis R. Dimick, *Asst. Dir.;* John A. Echave, *Research Grant Projects;* Elizabeth Cheng Krist, Bruce A. McElfresh, Kathy Moran, Kurt F. Mutchler, Richard Olsenius, Susan Welchman. **Layout and Design:** David Griffin, *Assoc. Dir.;* William H. Marr; *Typography:* Betty Clayman-DeAtley, Kay Kobor Hankins, Douglas M. McKenney. **Art:** Christopher A. Klein, *Artist;* Hillel J. Hoffmann, *Research.* **Engraving and Printing:** Janet C. Evans, *Director;* Judy L. Garvey, Randal G. Sluss

CARTOGRAPHY

John F. Shupe, *Chief Cartographer. Assoc. Director:* Marguerite B. Hunsiker; *Asst. Directors:* Kevin P. Allen, Frances H. Myers, Juan J. Valdés. *Geographer:* Alice T. M. Rechlin. *Editors:* Edward Easton, Maureen J. Flynn, Jonathan E. Kaut, David B. Miller, Gus Platis. *Designers:* Sally S. Summerall, *Supvr.;* Charles W. Berry, John A. Bonner, Robert E. Pratt, Nancy Schweickart. *Researchers:* Harold A. Hanson, *Supvr.;* Dierdre T. Bevington-Attardi, Mary Kate Cannistra, Deborah J. Gibbons, Linda R. Kriete, Lisa R. Ritter, Andrew J. Wahll. *Production:* Richard W. Bullington, Martin J. Golden, *Supvrs.;* Barbara P. Holland, Ellen J. Landsman, James E. McClelland, Jr., Daniel J. Ortiz, Stephen P. Wells, Alfred L. Zebarth. *Specialists:* Edward J. Holland, Ronald E. Williamson

EDITORIAL SERVICES

Administration: Neva L. Folk, *Asst. to the Editor;* Maria-Teresa Lawrence, *Business Manager;* Sara L. Anderson, Sandra M. Dane, Marisa Domeyko, Artemis S. Lampathakis, Rebecca Martin, Charlene S. Valeri, Kathy Williamson. *Control Center:* Carol L. Dumont, Alicia M. Schaner. *Travel:* Ann C. Judge, *Director.* **Audiovisual:** Joanne M. Hess, *Asst. Vice President and Director;* Ronald S. Altemus, Scott A. Brader, P. Andrew van Duym. **Communications:** Mary Jeanne Jacobsen, *Asst. Vice President, Public Affairs;* Joy Aschenbach, Barbara H. Fallon, Barbara S. Moffet, Benita M. Swash. **Information Services:** *Correspondence:* Joseph M. Blanton, Jr., *Director;* John A. Rutter. *Image Collection:* Maura A. Mulvihill, *Asst. Vice President and Director;* Carolyn J. Harrison; William D. Perry, *Image Sales. Library and Indexing:* Susan Fifer Canby, *Director;* Ann C. Benson, Ellen D. Briscoe, Carolyn Locke, Marta Strada. *Records:* Mary Anne McMillen, *Director;* Ann E. Hubbs. *Translations:* Kathryn A. Bazo

ADMINISTRATION

Asst. Vice Presidents: Christina C. Alberghini, Carolyn F. Clewell, Joseph S. Fowler, Angelo M. Grima, Douglas E. Hill, Robert E. Howell, Robert V. Koenig, Thomas E. Kulikosky, Carol E. Lang, Frances A. Marshall, Jennifer Moseley, Jimmie D. Pridemore, Stephen R. Vick. **Asst. Treasurer:** Barbara J. Constantz. **Assts. to the Chairman:** Karen L. Harshbarger, Karen S. Marsh. **Asst. to the President:** Marilyn J. Williams. **Accounting:** Michael J. Cole, *Asst. Vice President;* Chia-Chyi Cheng, Larry E. Dowdy, Barbara A. Finn, Janet C. Yates. **Administration:** David C. Beveridge, Mary L. Blanton, Delores J. Granberg, Carol A. Houck, Myra A. McLellan, R. Miles White, Barbara A. Williams. **Circulation:** Kitty Carroll Colbert, *Vice President;* Kathleen A. Gallagher. **Development Office:** Margaret Sears, *Director;* Dorothy R. Jacobson, Betsy Ellison. **Educational Services:** Robert L. Graham. **Explorers Hall:** Susan S. Norton, *Director;* Nancy W. Beers, Richard McWalters. **Foreign Editions:** Robert W. Hernandez, *Asst. Vice President and Director.* **Geography Education:** Robert E. Dulli, *Asst. Vice President and Director;* Mary Lee Elden, J. Joe Ferguson, Karen E. Gibbs, Roger B. Hirschland. **Human Resources:** Barbara Duckworth Case. **Information Systems:** James P. McCrystal, *Vice President;* Richard A. Mechler, *Asst. Vice President;* Scott Bolden, Warren Burger, William L. Chewning, Curtis L. Conway, Jr., Fred R. Hart, George F. Hubbs, Robert W. Madden. **Promotion:** Joan M. Anderson, James V. Bullard, Robert L. Feige, Charles F. Herrmann III, Deborah A. Jones

PRODUCTION SERVICES

Hans H. Wegner, *Asst. Vice President.* **Imaging Services:** Robert E. Allnutt. **Manufacturing:** George V. White, *Director;* John T. Dunn, *Assoc. Director.* **Pre-Press:** Geoffrey T. McConnell, *Director;* Martin G. Anderson, James C. Pflieger, Phillip E. Plude, Bernard G. Quarrick. **Printing:** Joseph M. Anderson, Sherrie S. Harrison, Diana L. Yates. **Quality:** Bill M. Aldridge, *Director.* **Administration:** Joan S. Simms

ADVERTISING

J. Scott Crystal, *Vice President and Director;* Ron Bottorff, *Western Manager;* Laurie L. Kutsche, *Chicago Manager;* Sherburne F. Naulty, *Eastern Manager;* Philip G. Reynolds, *Special Accounts and Southwest Manager;* Michel Siegfried, *International Director,* 90 Champs-Élysées, 75008 Paris; Andrea Vaughan, *Detroit Manager.* Washington: Sarita L. Moffat, *Asst. Vice President, Operations;* Renee S. Clepper, *Research and Marketing;* Gail M. Jackson, *Production;* Pandora B. Todd, *Promotion*

EDUCATIONAL SERVICES OF THE SOCIETY

Book Division: William R. Gray, *Vice President and Director;* Charles Kogod, *Asst. Director;* Barbara A. Payne, *Editorial Director;* John G. Agnone, Leah Bendavid-Val, Martha C. Christian, Elizabeth Newhouse, *Senior Editors.* **Traveler:** Richard Busch, *Editor;* Paul Martin, *Managing Editor; World:* Susan Mondshein Tejada, *Editor;* Scott S. Stuckey, *Managing Editor.* **Education Products:** David Beacom, *Director.* **Administration:** Suzanne R. McDowell, *Asst. Vice President;* Carolyn W. Jones

---

NATIONAL GEOGRAPHIC TELEVISION

Timothy T. Kelly, *President;* Todd Berman, *Marketing/Distr.;* Susan Borke, *Business Affairs;* Lowell Soffer, *Finance;* Andrew Wilk, *Programming/Production;* Patricia Gang, *Film Library;* Nicolas Noxon, *Exec. Producer, Specials;* Michael Rosenfeld, *Exec. Producer, Explorer;* Kathleen F. Teter, *Public Relations*

NATIONAL GEOGRAPHIC SOCIETY

"For the increase and diffusion of geographic knowledge."

It was a year of misery for Eastern Europeans, 1241.
To escape the Mongol juggernaut, 40,000 refugees from the
steppe of Russia had straggled into Hungary. Mongol forces
followed, smashing every army in their path. Only the
death of the great khan Ogodei back in Mongolia halted their
onslaught. Today the memory of Hungary's agony is
kept alive by a memorial near the town of Muhi, where 60,000
were killed during the spring of that terrible year.

SONS OF GENGHIS

THE GREAT KHANS

BY MIKE EDWARDS
ASSISTANT EDITOR

PHOTOGRAPHS BY JAMES L. STANFIELD

*R*uthless as the Mongols themselves, time has all but obliterated their once splendid capital of Karakorum. Today a stone tortoise announces that here, on the windblown steppe of central Mongolia, ruled a powerful dynasty of warrior kings. Forged from brutal conquests of China, Russia, and most of the Middle East, the 13th-century Mongol world was the largest land empire history has known. The paiza—an inscribed passport-medallion—allowed messengers to cross the empire's vast landscapes unimpeded. Though masters on land, the Mongols suffered great defeats at sea. Attempting to invade Japan, thousands died—some by drowning, others by fighting for a toehold on shore. A trophy from that battle, an embossed Mongol officer's helmet (left), is now a Japanese museum piece.

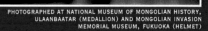

Survivor of Mongol wrath, the Cathedral of St. Sophia offered refuge for the people of Kiev during the invasion of their city by Batu, the grandson of Genghis and conqueror of Russia. Other Kievans found no such sanctuary. A silversmith's mold found with human remains under a sacked church testifies to its end as a tool to bring forth craft and delight.

TO EUROPEANS of the 13th century they were the horde from hell: Tartars from Tartarus, that part of Hades where the wicked were punished. They had the heads of dogs, and they devoured the bodies of their victims.

Indeed, the Tartars, as Europeans called the Mongols, sometimes did eat the raw hearts or livers of slain foes, hoping to capture their spirits. Europeans knew little about these invaders from the east, and "Tartars" seemed an apt name for them. It sounded like Tatar, a name that was commonly applied to peoples of the Asian steppe. Genghis Khan had slaughtered a tribe of Tatars in his rise to power in Mongolia.

Mongolia? Where was that? Even to learned Europeans the distant realms of Asia were terra incognita.

Dire warnings of the Mongols' approach reached Hungary's king, Béla IV, in 1236. Soon thousands of refugees poured into his kingdom, bringing news of the sacking of cities to the east.

For the genesis of the Mongol invasion of Europe we must leap 4,000 miles to Karakorum on Mongolia's steppe (map, pages 14-15). In a 20-year-long series of battles Genghis had brought the Merkits, Kereyits, and some 25 other Mongol tribes under his dominion, and by the time of his death in 1227 he had established Karakorum as his base. Now the mantle

of power had passed to his son Ogodei, who would expand on Genghis's achievements, sending Mongol armies rampaging both east and west.

I arrived at Harhorin, a small town near the site of Karakorum, to chants and the clash of cymbals. This was not in my honor, however. Buddhist monks in wine-colored robes were bestowing an annual blessing on the home of my host, Baruuzan Orosin, a hotelier of sorts, who rents round, felt-walled *gers* to visitors. I was ushered into his residence: three gers joined together. Crowded into one were eight monks and a dozen of Orosin's kin.

Orosin ladled bitter *koumiss,* fermented mare's milk, the ubiquitous drink of Mongolia, into pint-size bowls. His wife, Amarjargal, a buxom woman in a blue silk dress, handed the bowls to the guests along with plates of boiled mutton. Then the monks noticed me and, one after the other, began passing their snuff flasks, smiling and gesturing that I should sniff a few grains.

As I was trying to juggle all this hospitality, the monks began to chant again, and Orosin filled copper cups with vodka, another popular Mongolian drink. Chanting gave way to singing, laughing, and shouting that continued long after I had retired to my ger next door. At last there was silence, save for the wailing of a dog that made the steppe seem achingly lonely.

For a brief time in the 13th century Karakorum was the most powerful city in the world. But besides sherds of roof tiles and porcelain, little remains today; Chinese invaders destroyed the capital in 1388, after the Mongol empire had waned.

Stretched out on a cot in my ger, I peopled the silent rubble. Karakorum was home to Uygurs from what is now western China, who were employed as scribes and administrators, and probably to masons from the kingdom of Xi Xia and smiths from Samarkand, captured by Genghis. Because the Mongols were tolerant of all faiths, there were Buddhist monks, Muslim imams, Mongol shamans, and Nestorian Christians, the early proselytizers in east Asia.

Ogodei took the title khagan, "khan of khans"—lord of lords, as we would say. Genghis had chosen Ogodei as his successor shortly before he died, probably believing that Ogodei was the most competent of the four sons by his principal wife. Ogodei lived riotously, enjoying—like my partying friends in the next ger—feasts and drink. He built an enormous palace and commissioned a silver fountain adorned with animals, including an elephant, a tiger, and a horse, from which spurted koumiss, wine, and mead. According to Rashid ad-Din, a Persian who wrote about the Mongols, Ogodei took "pleasures in the company of beauteous ladies and moonfaced mistresses." But he was also his father's son, and soon after becoming khagan, Ogodei unleashed the army.

"Genghis never planned to create an empire," Larry Moses, a historian at Indiana University, believes. "But with Ogodei that changed. Genghis's sons had been granted territories of their own, and under Ogodei the Mongols began to enlarge them."

First, in 1230, troops reconquered Central Asia, the scene of so much destruction by Genghis himself, and then swept on to the modern lands of Azerbaijan, Georgia, Armenia, and Turkey. Rulers became vassals, paying tribute and supplying troops.

Even while those campaigns were under way, Ogodei led his cavalry against the Jin dynasty of northern China, whose territory Genghis had also plundered. The Mongol army was so formidable that it could fight on two fronts at once. In 1233 the Jin capital, Kaifeng, toppled, and a quarter of what is now China belonged to Karakorum. Some Mongols wanted to slaughter the Chinese and turn their land into pasture for horses. Ogodei, however, heeded a Chinese scholar who argued that if the people lived, and prospered, they could be taxed.

Thomas Allsen of Trenton State College in New Jersey, an expert on Mongol administration, has documented an array of taxes imposed on subject peoples. In China farmers were taxed according to the quality of their land and the number of oxen and tools they owned. There was also a head tax on adult males, payable in grain, and a household tax, payable in silk. Similar taxes were imposed elsewhere in the Mongol empire. Merchants were taxed on transactions. Special assessments, such as levies of flour or rice for the army, were not unusual, and newly conquered peoples could expect to hand over a tenth of their possessions.

Emboldened by success, in 1235 the Mongol nobles met at a *kuriltai*, or great assembly, and resolved to venture even farther afield. They would plunder the rich Southern Song empire and send yet another force westward—the army that reached Europe.

As Morris Rossabi, an Asia scholar at Columbia University and City University of New York, points out, "It wasn't a conscious decision to invade Europe. They didn't know exactly where they were heading." Historians believe the campaign was intended to secure the flanks of the fiefdom of Batu, one of Genghis's grandsons. An undefined western territory had been granted to Batu's father, Jochi, Genghis's eldest son.

Photographer JIM STANFIELD covered the emergence of the Mongol empire under Genghis Khan for our December 1996 issue.

Reenacting a 750-year-old horror, a lone trumpeter sounds an alarm every hour on the hour from the tower of St. Mary's Church in Kraków, Poland. Tradition says the same call to arms was heard on Palm Sunday in 1241 to alert the townsfolk that Mongols were about to storm their walls. The trumpeter ends his clarion mid-note, evoking the moment at which a Mongol arrow struck his medieval predecessor in the throat.

And who, brothers, fathers, and children, seeing this, God's inffiction on the whole Russian Land, does not lament?

—CHRONICLE OF NOVGOROD

SIXTY THOUSAND or more cavalrymen, along with bombardiers to work the mangonels, the giant catapults of siege warfare, started westward from Mongolia in 1236. A few months later this force reached the Volga River near today's Russian city of Kazan.

Today a dam at Kazan makes a lake so wide I can't see the opposite bank. In fact, for most of its length Mother Volga is a series of stairstep reservoirs—and a sewer for industrial and human waste.

BIBLIOTHÈQUE NATIONALE, PARIS

Beside the river— free-flowing then, of course—the Mongol horsemen fell upon the capital of the kingdom of Bulgar. Its rulers, kin of the Danube Bulgarians, ran a prosperous trade in amber, furs, and lumber. News of the Mongol attack horrified the Russian principalities farther west. The chronicler of Novgorod wrote that the "godless" invaders "slew all, both wives and children." Today the Bulgar capital is mostly rubble.

The Mongols probably wore looted Bulgar furs as they set out across the snowbound steppe toward Ryazan, 400 miles west. Princes of that city rode out to parley with the invaders. What tribute would the Mongols accept in exchange for sparing Ryazan? They demanded "a tenth of everything," even a tenth of the women and children, according to the *Chronicle of Novgorod*. "Only when none of us remain," the nobles answered defiantly. So the Mongols cut trees and surrounded Ryazan's walls with a stockade. Shielded from the defenders' arrows, mangonel crews bombarded the city with stones for five days. Then the Mongols poured in, engaging in an orgy of rape and pillage.

Russia at the time was a collection of principalities, so no great army opposed the invaders. Turning north, they reached Moscow, a minor town, and torched its wooden houses. Then they rode east to Vladimir, a prosperous trading city that supplied furs, fish, and iron products, including combination locks, to merchants of the Hanseatic League.*

I went the 135 miles from Moscow to Vladimir by highway. On the outskirts of the city rose a clutch of boxy apartment buildings, gray and depressing. But the old city core was low and graceful, pilastered, columned, and crowned with golden domes. A bulbous stone gatehouse stood athwart busy Moscow Street. In 1238 its gate was gold-sheathed— a touch of civic pride—and an earthen wall topped by a log stockade

Ignorance of east Asia led Europeans into wild imaginings of monstrous creatures. From India in the 14th century a papal envoy wrote: "No such people do exist as nations, though there may be an individual monster here and there." Headless denizens inhabit the east in this 15th-century illustration of Marco Polo's travels.

*See "The Hanseatic League, Europe's First Common Market," in the October 1994 issue.

MONGKE

KUBLAI

HULAGU

ARIGH BOKE

BATU

BERKE

GUYUK

TOLUI

JOCHI

CHAGHATAI

OGODEI

THE MONGOL DYNASTY

Husband to several wives, Genghis Khan fathered many children. The four sons by his principal wife, Borte, formed the limbs of his dynastic tree. The house of eldest son Jochi never produced a great khan, but it wielded great power. By his refusal to support Ogodei's line after the death of Guyuk, Jochi's son Batu forced a power shift to the Tolui house, thus opening the way for Mongke and Kublai. No images exist for Tolui, Berke, or Arigh Boke. Except for the hatted great khans, all are shown with traditional shaved heads.

GENGHIS

FOUR KHANS BESTRIDE ASIA

By the time of Kublai Khan the Mongol world had consolidated into four near-autonomous khanates, each the personal fief of one of Genghis Khan's descendants. After the defeat of the Jin and then the Southern Song empire, Kublai initiated 89 years of Mongol rule over China under the auspices of his Yuan dynasty. From the Yuan capital at Daidu, he remained titular head over the entire Mongol empire and active ruler over China and the Mongol homeland.

No match against the agile Mongols, European armies fall like sitting ducks during the battles of 1241–42. Showering their enemies with armor-piercing arrows, the Mongol cavalry then moves in to hack down the survivors with lance and hook.

EUROPEAN CAMPAIGN
Mongol raiding parties reach the outskirts of Vienna in December 1241. The death of Ogodei back in Mongolia saves Europe from further attack.

RUSSIANS
Batu subdued Russia's feuding principalities by 1240. They remain vassals until Ivan III repels the Mongols in 1480.

Baltic Sea

Legnica, 1241
POLAND
TEUTONIC KNIGHTS
• Novgorod

E U R O P E
POLISH PRINCIPALITIES
AUSTRIA
Vienna •
• Kraków
• Moscow
RUSSIAN PRINCIPALITIES
• Vladimir

Pannonhalma abbey
(Budapest) Buda
Mohi, 1241
Pest
HUNGARY
Vassal states
Chernigov (Chernihiv)
Kiev •
• Ryazan
(Kazan)
• Bulgar
1237

UKRAINE

1242

Adriatic Sea

BULGARIA

Black Sea

Caucasus Mountains

G O L D E N
Sarai
Golden Horde capital after 1242

Caspian Sea

Mediterranean Sea

TURKEY
SELJUK SULTANATE OF RUM
Vassal state, 1243
GEORGIA
ARMENIA
1269
AZERBAIJAN
UZBEKIST

Aral Sea

LESSER ARMENIA
Aleppo •
(Orumiyeh) •
• Tabriz
Ilkhanate capital after 1265
Maragheh
Ilkhanate capital until 1265
TURKMENISTA

Ain Jalut, 1260
Mamluks defeat Mongols
PALESTINE
Jerusalem
SYRIA
IRAQ
Elburz Mts.

1231

I L K H A N A T

MAMLUK SULTANATE
ABBASID
Baghdad
Abbasid capital falls, 1258
1257–58
1256
Herat

EGYPT

CALIPHATE
Conquered by Mongols, 1258

IRAN

P E R S I A

A F R I C A

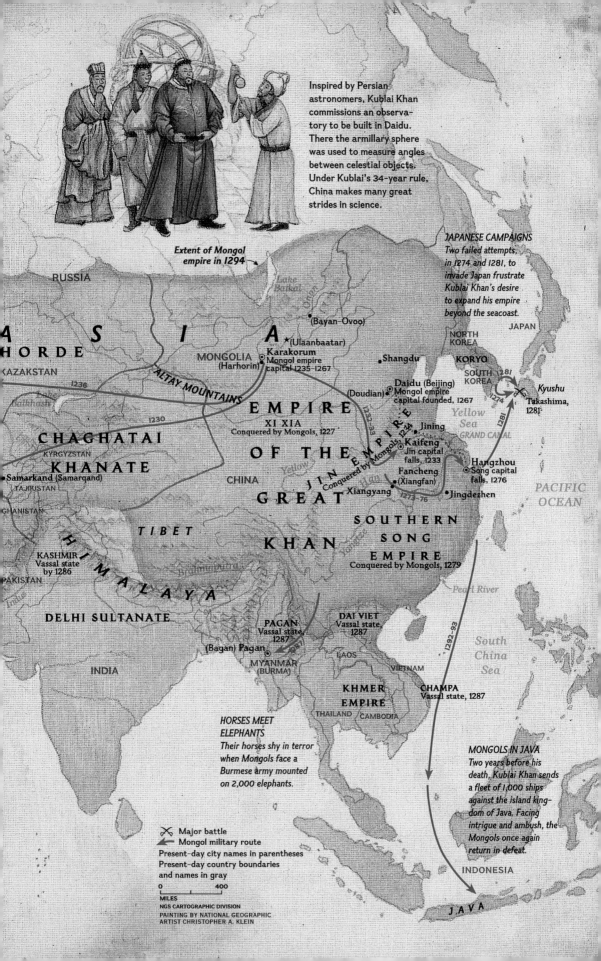

Inspired by Persian astronomers, Kublai Khan commissions an observatory to be built in Daidu. There the armillary sphere was used to measure angles between celestial objects. Under Kublai's 34-year rule, China makes many great strides in science.

Extent of Mongol empire in 1294

RUSSIA

Lake Baikal

ASIA

HORDE

KAZAKSTAN

1236

Balkhash

1230

CHAGHATAI

KYRGYZSTAN

KHANATE

Samarkand (Samarqand)

TAJIKISTAN

AFGHANISTAN

PAKISTAN

KASHMIR
Vassal state
by 1286

HIMALAYA

Indus

DELHI SULTANATE

INDIA

(Bayan-Ovoo)

★(Ulaanbaatar)

MONGOLIA
(Harhorin)

Karakorum
Mongol empire
capital 1235-1267

(Doudian)

EMPIRE

XI XIA
Conquered by Mongols, 1227

OF THE

CHINA

Yellow

GREAT

Xiangyang

TIBET

KHAN

Brahmaputra

SOUTHERN

SONG

EMPIRE
Conquered by Mongols, 1279

Yangtze

PAGAN
Vassal state
1287

(Bagan) Pagan

MYANMAR
(BURMA)

DAI VIET
Vassal state,
1287

LAOS

VIETNAM

KHMER
EMPIRE

THAILAND / CAMBODIA

CHAMPA
Vassal state, 1287

•Shangdu

Daidu (Beijing)
Mongol empire
capital founded, 1267

Jining

JIN EMPIRE
Conquered by Mongols 1234

Kaifeng
Jin capital
falls, 1233

Fancheng
(Xiangfan)

1273-76

•Jingdezhen

NORTH
KOREA

KORYO

SOUTH
KOREA

Yellow
Sea

GRAND CANAL

Hangzhou
Song capital
falls, 1276

Pearl River

South
China
Sea

1292-93

JAPANESE CAMPAIGNS
Two failed attempts,
in 1274 and 1281, to
invade Japan frustrate
Kublai Khan's desire
to expand his empire
beyond the seacoast.

JAPAN

1281

Kyushu
Takashima,
1281

1274

1281

PACIFIC
OCEAN

MONGOLS IN JAVA
Two years before his
death, Kublai Khan sends
a fleet of 1,000 ships
against the island king-
dom of Java. Facing
intrigue and ambush, the
Mongols once again
return in defeat.

INDONESIA

JAVA

HORSES MEET
ELEPHANTS
Their horses shy in terror
when Mongols face a
Burmese army mounted
on 2,000 elephants.

⚔ Major battle
→ Mongol military route
Present-day city names in parentheses
Present-day country boundaries
and names in gray

0   400
MILES

NGS CARTOGRAPHIC DIVISION
PAINTING BY NATIONAL GEOGRAPHIC
ARTIST CHRISTOPHER A. KLEIN

stretched from the gatehouse around the city. In February of that year the townsfolk peered in terror from the battlements as Mongol horsemen approached across the snowbound countryside.

I imagine standing with them. We see the invaders dismount and advance behind a shield of captives. Some Mongols rain arrows on us, others batter the gate with a great log. It makes a terrible noise like thunder. The mangonels hurl burning stuff that smells of sulfur and oil. Looking behind me, I see my house afire. Many of the other wooden houses are in flames too.

Our ruler, Prince Yuri, was slain when he went to seek help, so we cannot expect another prince to aid us. We do what we can to drive away the heathens. (As devout Christians, we believe the Mongols are godless savages.) When they lean ladders against our wall and start to climb, we pour boiling water and resin on them. We throw down stones, anything. Many Mongols die, but others keep coming. Then our stockade catches fire, and the Mongols burst through the burning timbers.

I hide in a cellar. Some of my companions retreat into Assumption Cathedral, which is built like a fortress: a cube of stone with narrow windows. The Mongols fight their way in. Our poor Princess Agafya. And her daughter and grandchildren. Somehow the Mongols know that Prince Yuri's family is hiding in the loft. They set fires to smoke them out. Defiant to the end, Agafya suffocates with her kin.

The Mongols plunder whatever they want: the coveted locks made by our smiths, silver candlesticks, even the candles. They strip what's left of the golden gate. They take our wives and sisters.

Remarkably, some 760 years later Assumption Cathedral still stands in Vladimir. A marble slab in a wall marks the niche where the bodies of Princess Agafya and her family were interred.

> *The Mongols, like a brave lion falling upon its prey, pursued them, smiting and slaying. . . .*
>
> —RASHID AD-DIN: DEFEAT OF THE HUNGARIANS

T
HE WAVE OF DESTRUCTION swept across Ukraine, consuming Kiev and Chernigov. Between assaults the Mongols paused for almost a year to fatten their horses and forge new arms. They probably collected fresh troops from among the Kipchaks and other Turkic tribes on the steppe.

Meanwhile scouts gathered intelligence in the west. Hungary's army was potentially huge—perhaps 100,000 troops if King Béla could rely on his quarrelsome barons to fight. In Poland a sizable army was garrisoned at Kraków and another at Legnica. When the Mongols set out again, in February 1241, their leader, Batu, spread his forces across a 600-mile front, intending to engage all of them in one great sweep.

Thirty thousand cavalry rode into Poland. A vanguard approached Kraków, then retreated—a favorite Mongol tactic. Polish troops came out in pursuit, only to blunder into the ambush. The defenseless city was torched on Palm Sunday.

Near Legnica, Duke Henry, one of Poland's four ruling princes, fell into a similar trap. His 30,000 men included a contingent of Teutonic Knights from the Baltic region, covered from head to toe in heavy steel mail. The Mongols appeared and retreated. The mounted knights rushed in pursuit, only to find themselves in the pall of a smoke screen. Blinded and encumbered by their metal sheathing, the knights fell to fast-charging wielders of mace and lance. Henry's army was destroyed.

*B*read was a novelty for the Mongols in Herat, Afghanistan. Bakers like Habibullah still produce the flat loaves of unleavened nan *that Hulagu and his army might have sampled when they passed through the city in 1256*

Hungary too felt the Mongol scourge, though you would never guess it from the look of Budapest today. The city endured other onslaughts—Turks invaded in the 1500s, and German and Soviet armies fought over it in World War II—but it has always risen anew. Now it has changed again from the charming but rather gloomy place I had known when it was under the Soviet Union's domination. The crenellated Fishermen's Bastion still invites lovers to stroll overlooking the Danube, but all around I see the trappings of capitalism: nightclubs, casinos, flashing neon, and billboards advertising American jeans.

Buda and Pest were separate cities, divided by the Danube, when Batu's scouts rode up to Pest, on the left bank, in March 1241. King Béla, meanwhile, was trying to coax his barons to face the danger. They had been feuding about power. The monarchy had declined under Béla's father, and Béla was attempting to reassert his authority, even confiscating baronial estates. Another dispute had boiled up over the hordes of Cuman steppe nomads who had poured into Hungary ahead of the Mongol advance. The barons resented Béla's offer of refuge to these foreigners.

on their way to subdue the Abbasid caliphate. Pastoralists, the Mongols disdained people who worked the soil. Their diet consisted almost totally of meat and dairy products—a menu that persists today.

Still, some of the nobles had come to Buda and Pest with their troops, and Batu, learning of the wall of Pest, probably concluded that a siege would be difficult, while open-field warfare might yield a decisive victory. So he ordered his soldiers to retreat. Encouraged by this, Béla's nobles fell into line and set out with their monarch in cautious pursuit.

I traced the armies' route from Budapest 135 miles northeast to the Muhi plain, tranquil farm country stippled with red-roofed villages and chestnut trees. On the little Sajo River a two-car ferry slid back and forth on a cable. Somewhere near this stream King Béla bivouacked and circled his camp with wagons. They came out to meet Batu's army, and for a time the Hungarians had the better of the fight. But then one wing of Batu's force got behind them. Surrounded, the Hungarians broke out and fell back to their tightly drawn camp.

For the Mongols the battle became like a great hunt at home, when riders drove prey into a circle to be slaughtered. They poured arrows and flaming missiles into the packed mass, setting wagons and tents on fire. The Hungarians fled, only to be cut down. Before the day was done,

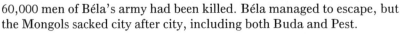

60,000 men of Béla's army had been killed. Béla managed to escape, but the Mongols sacked city after city, including both Buda and Pest.

ON A HIGH HILL 110 miles west of Buda, monks in the Benedictine abbey of Pannonhalma measured the approach of the dreaded horsemen by smoke plumes rising from villages and towns. The abbey had been standing on that hill for 245 years when the Mongols arrived.

To me, as I drove toward the abbey on a poplar-shaded lane, it resembled a great stone fortress, which is also how it appeared to the Mongols. I went inside and met Gaspar Csoka, the abbey librarian, who withdrew a sheaf of yellowed records from a safe. He spread the documents on a table and began to tell me about Pannonhalma's 13th-century abbot, whose name was Uros. The records reveal a man of resolve who had spent years renovating the abbey church: "Not a man to surrender," said Csoka. "When the Mongols came, I'm sure Uros took part in the fight."

We went up to the rampart that circles the church. From there, Csoka believes, monks and peasants fired arrows at their Mongol besiegers, with old Uros—he was about 70—in the thick of it.

Bastions of early terrorism, the Assassins' fortresses in northern Iran were Hulagu's targets after he launched his campaign to the west. He first defeated the Assassins, an extremist Islamic sect, and then the 500-year-old Abbasid caliphate. Founder of his own khanate, he was heir

to a civilization famous
for crafts, such as the
wool carpets still woven
in northern Iran.
Hulagu spared the Chris-
tians when he attacked
Baghdad in 1258. His
mother was a Nestorian
Christian, a faith surviving among some 400,000
adherents, like these in
Orumiyeh, Iran.

Apparently surprised by the spirited defense, the Mongols withdrew.

Batu's raiding parties crossed into Austria, almost reaching Vienna. Some historians speculate that the Mongols could have driven much deeper into Europe. But in 1242 a rider from Karakorum reached Batu with the news that Khagan Ogodei was dead (most likely from drink), and suddenly the Mongols were gone.

Batu probably withdrew because he expected his uncle's death to touch off a struggle for the throne. Larry Moses says Batu aspired to be khagan but knew that Ogodei's son, Guyuk, had been preordained. And Batu hated him. Still, Guyuk would have to be confirmed at a kuriltai of nobles, and if Batu, an honored khan, did not return to Karakorum to take part, the confirmation might be thwarted. Since he was heir to the Mongols' western lands, Batu decided to retire to southern Russia and build his own capital.

The sacking of Baghdad sent tremors through the Islamic world. Aided by vassal states, Hulagu's troops crushed the defending garrison in open combat, then proceeded to bombard the city with mangonels—like the one seen at lower left in a 14th-century illustration that depicts soldiers crossing a river by means of a pontoon bridge. Once inside, they wrapped the Abbasid caliph in a carpet and trampled him with horses. They plundered Islam's greatest city, killing anyone who resisted.

Sarai, as it was called, must have been spectacular, for Russian archaeologists have unearthed fine glazed tiles and even clay water pipes. Batu ruled from a huge ger. Legend says it was lined with gold brocade and inspired the name for Batu's Russian realm, Golden Horde. (The word "horde" comes from the Mongol *ordu*—camp or fiefdom.)

The Golden Horde allowed the Russian princes to administer their own territories but extracted taxes and troops in tribute. Russian historians call this the "Tatar yoke." If the levies were withheld, the Mongols burned the cities again or summoned the recalcitrant princes to Sarai, where some were killed. Prince Mikhail of Chernigov, for example, was kicked to death and beheaded for good measure.

The Mongols in Sarai were outnumbered by Kipchaks and other Turkic people of the steppe, who were soldiers, tax collectors, and slaves. Today their descendants are among the six million people who in Russia are still called Tatars.

The dynasty did not have a sitting monarch for quite a while. Within and without there was great tumult.

—CHINESE HISTORICAL TEXT

ITH OGODEI'S DEATH, and with Batu opposing the choice of Guyuk and refusing to return to Mongolia for a kuriltai, the descendants of Genghis were thrown into confusion. "If no acceptable candidate could be agreed upon, they simply fought it out and whoever won, won," says Thomas Allsen of Trenton State.

After Ogodei's death they did not fight with weapons, though that would come later. What transpired was rough-and-ready politicking, with deals and favors—fiefdoms, treasure, concubines—dispensed to princes and nobles in exchange for allegiance.

In the main, the house of Ogodei was arrayed against that of his brother Tolui. In each clan a powerful woman played the leading role. Although men took several wives and had concubines, one wife, usually the first, enjoyed high status and frequently took part in clan affairs.

In fact, Ogodei's widow Toregene ruled the empire for three years after his death, all the while scheming to win the throne for her son, Guyuk. Historians portray her as a vindictive woman with a penchant for sorcery. The other woman in the succession contest was Tolui's widow Sorghaghtani, described as politically savvy—a Christian who supported Islam with alms. Ultimately her candidate was her son Mongke.

Round one went to Toregene, who in 1246 saw Guyuk enthroned in a

he citadel at Aleppo looked down in stony defiance when the Mongols stormed through Syria in 1260. Behind its ramparts the elderly Turan Shah held out for more than a month, long after the rest of the city had fallen. Out of respect for such fortitude, the invaders spared his life.

J̶uiciest plum in southern China, the city of Hangzhou was treated like a trophy by Kublai Khan when he conquered it in 1276. Largest city in the world by some estimates, the Song capital teemed with at least one million people. Parks and pavilions grace a lakefront

ger outside Karakorum. In attendance was a Franciscan friar, Giovanni da Pian del Carpini, who traveled deep into Asia 28 years before Marco Polo. He wrote that Mongol nobles and vassal rulers "brought to the new emperor an infinite quantity of gold, silver, precious stones and other valuables," and "general revelries . . . went on well into the night."

Giovanni was about 65 when he made his 15-month journey through devastated eastern Europe and across Mongol-held Central Asia to deliver a letter from Pope Innocent IV. The pope wanted assurance that Europe would not be invaded again and invited the Mongols to accept Christianity, but Guyuk gave no promise of restraint and rejected baptism. Instead, he said Innocent IV should lead a delegation of kings "to pay homage to me and to serve me."

Guyuk, another hard drinker, ruled only two years. Now a new succession struggle began. Guyuk's widow strove to win the khanship for her nephew Shiremun. But this time powerful nobles sided with Sorghaghtani, and Mongke was enthroned at a kuriltai in 1251. Even as the nobles celebrated, Shiremun and his supporters approached the ceremonial tent with arms, only to be discovered at the last minute and arrested.

Mongke exiled Shiremun to China, where he was later executed, and

stained the far corners of the empire with the blood of suspect cousins and their collaborators. Some were murdered in darkly ingenious ways; two officials choked as their mouths were stuffed with stones, and Guyuk's widow was sewn in a carpet and drowned.

Mongke consolidated his grip on power by cloaking himself in Genghis Khan's mantle, proclaiming, "I follow the laws of my ancestors." This was certain to appeal in Karakorum, where people had begun to worship idols of Genghis.

He is still revered. Last spring before Mongolia's parliamentary elections, the Democratic Union Coalition aired TV commercials in which a Genghis look-alike declared that if Genghis Khan were alive, he'd be on the coalition's side. The coalition won decisively.

"I believe he really thought of his grandfather as his guide," Thomas Allsen says of Mongke. "I think he believed he must continue Genghis's policies." And that meant conquest.

Mangonel-men . . . with a stone missile would convert the eye of a needle into a passage for a camel. —JUVAINI

MONGKE LAUNCHED CAMPAIGNS even more audacious than Genghis had imagined. He and his brother Kublai led renewed assaults on the Song dynasty in southern China. From their capital, Hangzhou, probably the world's largest city, with at least one million people, the Song ruled an empire rich in silk, jade, and porcelain. They printed books and sent trading ships to Java and India. Fertile lands along the Yangtze, Pearl, and other rivers fed 50 million people.

The Middle East was an equally tempting target, renowned for its carpets, calligraphy, and scholars, including mathematicians, astronomers, and physicians. So another brother, Hulagu, was sent west to capture Baghdad, Islam's greatest city, as well as lands along the Mediterranean.

In 1253 the Persian writer Ala-ad-Din Ata-Malik Juvaini recorded Hulagu's preparations for his Baghdad expedition. With the cavalry were a thousand expert artillerymen from China. The army swelled with troops from vassal states: Armenians, Georgians, Persians, Turks. By one estimate the force grew to 150,000 men, perhaps the largest one the Mongols ever put afield.

Hulagu veered into the Elburz Mountains to destroy the Assassins, a violent Islamic sect. Dagger-wielding fanatics, the Assassins had murdered many Islamic rulers who rejected their extremist tenets. They were said to strike while under the influence of hashish—hence the word "assassin," from the Arabic *hashshashin,* or hashish eaters.

Juvaini recorded that the mangonels hammered the eagles-nest fortress of the sect's grand master, Rukn ad-Din, until he surrendered. He asked to be allowed to travel to Mongke's court to seek clemency, and Hulagu agreed. But in Karakorum Rukn ad-Din was received coldly, and after he departed the city, Juvaini wrote, he was "kicked to a pulp and then put to the sword."

The Mongol juggernaut rolled on to Baghdad and the verdant lands along the Tigris. Genghis had always been fortunate in facing enemies weakened by internal problems, and in 1258 the Mongol luck held for Hulagu. Baghdad's ruler, Caliph Mustasim, was lethargic and insulated, and his chief minister was of doubtful loyalty. On the one occasion that the caliph's troops ventured forth, the Mongols broke a dike behind them, trapping them with floodwaters, and killed at least 12,000.

once fringed with palaces. Signaling the end of a long conquest, the seizure of Hangzhou followed a softening in Mongol behavior. Kublai spared the city's inhabitants, and the surrendering Song court was allowed to retain some of its wealth and privilege.

*B*uddhist novices chant their prayers with a drum at a temple in the Mongolian village of Bayan-Ovoo, claimed by locals to be the birthplace of Genghis Khan. Mongols accepted all religions, and Kublai allowed the unhindered practice of Buddhism when he founded China's Yuan dynasty.

Hulagu's mangonels hurled palm-tree stumps against Baghdad (carts hauling stone missiles had not arrived), and after seven days the walls were breached. The Mongols poured in. The caliph's remaining soldiers were slaughtered, and there was civilian carnage reminiscent of Genghis's ravishing of Central Asia. Historians say that Christian Georgians and Armenians in Hulagu's army vented their hatred of Islam until Baghdad was filled with the stench of corpses. Some Persian writers put the toll as high as two million, an exaggeration, though it was certainly huge. "Many tens of thousands were killed," wrote a Chinese envoy who visited Baghdad a year after its capture. Baghdad never recovered its place as the hub of Islamic culture. As for the caliph, he and his sons were sewn in carpets and trampled to death by horses.

The Islamic world was in shock, as Europe had been when Batu scourged Hungary and Poland. The Mongols, who intended to stay, named Hulagu's territory, which included most of what is today Iraq and Iran, the Ilkhanate—"subordinate khanate." Soon Hulagu added Syria as well.

Christians in the Mongol army urged Hulagu to push on to capture Jerusalem, which was then in Muslim hands. Only one formidable foe,

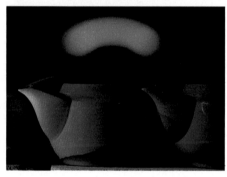

*C*hinese invention, a
potter's wheel spins off
a fresh creation under the
hands of He Qiou Shen
in the city of Jingdezhen.
Predating the Mongols
by a thousand years, the
city's porcelain industry
continues to turn out
fine ceramics, like this
kiln-ready teapot. Under
Kublai Khan, exports of
Chinese crafts flowered.
To bring rice to the
people of his northern
capital, he extended
China's Grand Canal,
seen near Jining.

the Mamluk regime of Egypt, stood in the way, and Hulagu demanded
its surrender. There was, however, another force present: crusaders
who clung to Palestine's Mediterranean shore, also hoping to gain
the Holy City. Would they side with the invaders from the east against
the Muslims?

Before the question could be answered, history repeated itself. Hulagu
learned that Khagan Mongke was dead, probably of dysentery, after a
reign of eight years. Hulagu anticipated a succession struggle, and, as
Batu had in Hungary, he withdrew, leaving only 10,000 troops to hold
the empire's Mediterranean frontier.

Qutuz, the Mamluk sultan, was determined to drive the Mongols away
and even invited the crusaders to join him in the campaign. The Christians spurned him but allowed the Mamluks to pass through their territory to attack the Mongol force.

At Ain Jalut in Galilee, where David is said to have killed Goliath, the
Mongols were lured into the kind of trap they had so often sprung. Seeing
the Mamluks retreat, they pursued, only to be surrounded and slaughtered. By Mongol standards this was no titanic clash—but it was a defeat.
Where Goliath had reached his limit, the Mongols reached theirs.

In Xanadu did Kubla Khan
A stately pleasure-dome decree:
Where Alph, the sacred river, ran
Through caverns measureless to man. . . .

—SAMUEL TAYLOR COLERIDGE, "KUBLA KHAN"

One of history's great misadventures unfolds in a 13th-century Japanese scroll depicting the attempted Mongol invasions of Japan. Undaunted by an aborted attack in 1274—when a storm forced his fleet to retreat—Kublai Khan launched a much larger armada against the islands in 1281. Again nature intervened, this time with a typhoon so

KUBLAI, then 44 years old, was leading an army on the banks of the Yangtze in Song territory when a rider brought news of Mongke's death. He soon heard, too, that his youngest brother, Arigh Boke, was maneuvering in Karakorum to become the new khagan. Kublai broke off the fight with the Song but instead of returning to Karakorum, where he believed his brother would take him prisoner, he withdrew to northern China.

When the Mongols captured this realm from the Jin, Kublai, as a grandson of Genghis, had been granted a share of the spoils: huge fiefdoms of land and peasants. He spent much of his life in China, surrounded by Confucian advisers and attending to the welfare of his peasants. He even built a capital there, complete with a dazzling palace. It stood in what today is China's Inner Mongolia Autonomous Region and was called Shangdu—the "Xanadu" of Coleridge's poem.

In Karakorum, Arigh Boke no doubt bore down on Kublai's attachment to China—evidence that Kublai had forsaken his roots—as he campaigned to become khagan. But Kublai moved faster, proclaiming himself khagan at Shangdu in May 1260. Only a month later (perhaps after receiving news of Kublai's preemptive strike), Arigh Boke proclaimed himself khagan at Karakorum. Kublai set out for Mongolia, fought a series of battles with Arigh Boke, and won his submission in 1264. Kublai spared his brother but executed ten of his advisers.

Kublai claimed to rule all the lands where Mongols held sway, from Korea to Iraq and Russia. But in fact the empire had splintered. While Kublai attacked Arigh Boke, another clash had erupted in the west.

Hulagu, lord of the Ilkhanate, and Berke, who had followed his brother Batu as ruler of the Golden Horde, warred over possession of the fine grasslands of Azerbaijan. Absorbed in their own affairs, the western chieftains paid only nominal homage to far-off Kublai. And soon their kin who ruled in Central Asia began to act independently as well.

The every-prince-for-himself greed of Genghis's sons and grandsons had already been exposed in the succession struggles; personal power and wealth were more important to them than any notion of greater Mongolia. Genghis, who had spent two decades unifying the Mongol tribes, must have screamed curses on his progeny from the grave.

F OR HIS PART Kublai concentrated on developing China. Following the tradition of his adopted land, he proclaimed himself founder of a Chinese dynasty, which he named Yuan—"origin" or "primal." Ever the builder, he began in 1267 to raise a new capital. The site he chose was more centrally located than Shangdu. He called it Daidu—"great capital." We know it today as Beijing.

"No Kublai, no Beijing" was the history lesson offered to me by Chen Gaohua, a scholar specializing in the Yuan dynasty, as we ate lunch in a Beijing restaurant. Chen pointed out that although several earlier dynasties had ruled from the plain where Beijing stands, Kublai's city was much larger, enclosed by a wall 18 miles around. And after his short-lived Yuan dynasty was overthrown by the Ming dynasty in 1368, succeeding dynasties kept Beijing as the capital. Chen reached with his chopsticks for another slice of Peking duck and added, with a touch of hyperbole, "We are dining in this restaurant thanks to Kublai."

The Yuan dynasty wall encompassed what is now the heart of Beijing, crowded with shops and office and apartment towers. Within Kublai's city, too, is historic Tiananmen Square, where Mao Zedong proclaimed the establishment of the People's Republic of China in 1949—and where, in 1989, a pro-democracy demonstration was crushed by tanks.

powerful that the Japanese called it kamikaze, *or divine wind. Along with 4,000 ships, Kublai lost at least 100,000 men, both at sea and on shore. In the seven years between invasions Japan's warriors—seen attacking a Mongol vessel—had learned to fight, like the Mongols, as a team.*

I usually got up early in Beijing and took a walk. I passed old women sweeping the alleys with bundles of twigs and saw sidewalk eateries springing to life, the coal smoke of braziers mingling with the aroma of steamed buns. Not far from my hotel stretched the high wall of the Forbidden City, the Ming stronghold. A little beyond that was Beihai Park, where couples paddled in rented boats on a placid lake.

Kublai knew that lake; it was on the grounds of his palace—"the greatest palace that ever was," Marco Polo wrote, with a banquet hall for 6,000. There were quarters for each of Kublai's four wives as well as for his many concubines. Kublai, Polo claimed, fathered 22 sons by his wives. (There was no tally of daughters.)

Some Western historians have questioned whether Marco Polo ever traveled to China, suggesting that he based his descriptions on other chronicles. But Chinese historians find in his text obscure names and facts that ancient Chinese records corroborate. To Daidu, Polo said, "are brought articles of greater cost and rarity, and in greater abundance . . . than to any other city in the world." From India came spices and pearls, and "no day in the year passes that there do not enter the city 1,000 cart-loads of silk" from China's provinces.

While encouraging trade, Chinese historians declare, Kublai also devoted great energy to improving the lot of farmers. "Before Kublai, the Mongols thought of farmers as useless people," says Chen Gaohua. "But Kublai appreciated them. He knew how to rule a farming country." He created an agriculture ministry that distributed seeds and animals. Farmers were encouraged to band together in communes.

Kublai would surely have admired the slight man, wearing a blue Mao jacket, whom I met in the village of Doudian near Beijing. As Doudian's longtime leader, Zhang Zhenliang has revolutionized his village. I saw luxuriant fields of cabbage, emerald carpets of sprouting wheat, and a river of golden corn spread out to dry on a roadside. All pointed to the benefits of good leadership and the use of tractors, fertilizers, and improved seeds. "Fifteen years ago it took 1,200 people to grow our food," Zhang said, "Today we need only 60." Villagers who once worked the land now have factory jobs, some producing clothing for export.

T HOUGH KUBLAI usually heeded the humane tenets of his Confucian advisers, he ignored them when they urged pacifism. He knew that in the eyes of both Mongols and Chinese his prestige would be measured in large part by the wealth and territory he added to his realm.

The most tempting target was the fertile Southern Song empire. Possession of the Song lands had long been a Mongol goal, and many Chinese themselves hoped that the south could be reunited with the north. (They had been joined until the collapse of the Tang dynasty in 907.) As early as 1260, the year he proclaimed himself khagan, Kublai had sent an emissary to woo the Song rulers in their capital, Hangzhou. He hoped the rulers would become his vassals. Instead, his emissary was taken captive.

Skirmishes erupted, then full-scale battles. Kublai's troops besieged two key cities, Xiangyang and Fancheng, for nearly five years. On opposite banks of the Han River in what is now Hubei Province, they guarded the Yangtze Basin, the Song rice bowl. The large Song navy supplied the besieged cities and patrolled the rivers and the seacoast. To confront these fleets, the Mongols assembled a navy of their own. Many of Kublai's sailors and some of his commanders were Chinese, and Chinese and Koreans built his ships. One of Kublai's nephews, who ruled the Ilkhanate, sent

*V*ictim of Mongol imperialism, the Burmese city of Pagan was conquered after its king refused tribute to Kublai Khan. Following the Mongol invasion of 1287, the Buddhist "city of four million temples" was abandoned to snakes and scorpions.

engineers to build monster mangonels. The stones they hurled may have weighed as much as 200 pounds.

Fancheng, heavily damaged by these machines, fell in 1273, and its sister city, Xiangyang, surrendered. Kublai now put the army under the command of a Turk named Bayan, who had served the Mongols in the Middle East campaign. Bayan fought relentlessly toward Hangzhou, capturing it in 1276. Three years later the last Song holdouts were defeated. Kublai had reunited China. He ordered the army to treat the people gently, meaning to win them over, not wipe them out.

Elsewhere in Southeast Asia and on the island of Java, Kublai's generals fared less well. Unused to tropical warfare, they depleted the Yuan treasury in several failed campaigns. With Kublai's death in 1294 Mongol expansion came to an end.

HANGZHOU is the southern terminus of the Grand Canal, an artery that, at my first glance, didn't seem deserving of the name. The water was the color of pea soup, and the canal was clotted with small boats from which laundry flapped like pennants. Their cargoes were basic: cement, sand, rolls of steel wire. I watched men unloading barges filled with bricks, carrying 40 at a time—a 120-pound load—in bamboo hods across their shoulders.

Begun centuries before Kublai's time, the canal was a grand endeavor. Dug by hand and gradually extended until it stretched more than a thousand miles, it was one of China's great construction projects. China's major rivers flow from west to east, so an interior north-south waterway meant that merchants could avoid sending their cargoes on the high seas, where pirates were always a threat.

The Grand Canal was inaccessible from Daidu, a problem Kublai solved by putting three million laborers to work. Extended 135 miles, the canal ensured a supply of rice for the north, where—despite Kublai's encouragement of agriculture—famine was a certainty if crops failed.

Even with the completion of the canal, Kublai's final years were filled with frustration. Still intent on expanding his rule, in 1281 he sent an armada of 4,400 ships and nearly 150,000 troops against Japan. Unable to make headway on Kyushu, the Mongols reboarded their vessels and attacked a smaller island, Takashima. But before they had gained more than a foothold, a typhoon roared in, sinking nearly all of Kublai's fleet. In all, two-thirds of his troops perished, the worst loss in Mongol history.

In 1292 Kublai tried to reach even farther—to Java, 2,000 miles south of China. He had sent an emissary to demand tribute from Java's king. Instead, the offended monarch branded the emissary's face. Kublai dispatched 1,000 ships and 20,000 troops. But the army was ambushed and withdrew after losing 3,000 men.

THESE HUMILIATIONS ate away at Mongol prestige, just as the cost of them depleted Kublai's treasury. Nevertheless when Kublai died, in 1294 at the age of 79, he bequeathed a unified China that had known the benefits of benevolent leadership.

Morris Rossabi, whose biography of Kublai is the definitive work, says, "Kublai was like other Mongol rulers in that he was a conqueror. But he also was able to govern, and he governed very astutely."

The usual succession disputes plagued Kublai's descendants in the weakening Yuan dynasty. Weary of burdensome taxes, inept rule, and corruption, Chinese commoners overthrew the Yuan lords in 1368, compelling them to return to Mongolia.

In Baghdad the Mongol Ilkhanate did not survive even that long; the last of Hulagu's line died in 1335. In Central Asia a Turkic lord, Timur, or Tamerlane, forged a new empire with his capital at Samarkand. The last remnant of the withered Golden Horde was overrun by a Turkic khan in 1502.

The Ming rulers who forced the Mongols out of China immediately began building fortifications to prevent them from returning. Walls to bar invaders had existed in China for centuries, but none was so formidable as the one the Ming eventually constructed. Harnessing the labor of millions, they built and built, for 200 years.

Forty miles north of Beijing, I walked on the parapet on a frigid day, the wind clutching at my throat as I traced the 2,500-mile-long wall's trajectory across the distant mountains. In every lookout tower, in every bowman's notch, fear is palpable: the fear that the Mongols struck in all who defended against their thundering horsemen.

Though at times the Mongols were constructive, uniting Mongolia, uniting China, and building Beijing, and though they were audacious and brave, their record is overwhelmingly one of greed and cruelty, of cities devastated—Samarkand, Herat, Baghdad—and nations subjugated. The Great Wall, as formidable in its way as the people it was built to keep out, is the Mongols' epitaph in stone. □

A virtual deity in his homeland, Genghis Khan inspires reverence at his memorial in northeast Mongolia. Condemned as an imperialist by the Soviets—whose own imperialism controlled Mongolian politics for 70 years—Genghis came from a time when conquest still earned grudging respect. Free now to write their own history, Mongolians resurrect the long-suppressed conqueror and hail him as a great unifier—the father of their nation, and a spirit waiting to be reborn.

To learn more about the Mongol empire, log on to National Geographic Online (http://www.nationalgeographic.com on the World Wide Web or GO NATIONAL GEOGRAPHIC on CompuServe).

An Arctic Breakthrough

Heralding a new era of cooperation, the United States and Russia are making data from their Cold War intelligence archives available to science.

FOR NEARLY HALF A CENTURY the intelligence agencies and military commands of the United States and the Soviet Union spent billions of dollars to collect information about the Arctic Ocean—everything from the properties of seawater and the topography of the seafloor to the seasonal patterns of sea ice.

Taken as a whole, this treasure trove might yield answers to profound questions about the Arctic and its relationship to the ecosystem of our planet. And yet, for national security reasons, the information was held strictly off-limits to environmental scientists around the world.

In the spirit of the new openness that followed the end of the Cold War, I became determined to do all that I could to help unlock access to beneficial knowledge, including the Arctic data. After I conferred with the national security community in Washington and with my counterpart and valued colleague, Prime Minister Viktor Chernomyrdin, in Moscow, both countries agreed to make much of the Arctic information available for use in peaceful scientific research.

I am proud to announce in these pages that we have taken a major step toward that goal. The first volume of the joint U.S.-Russian Arctic Ocean Atlas in CD-ROM format is hereby released to the world's scientific community. And we offer in the following article a representative selection from the CD-ROM.

With this atlas some of science's most sought-after data about our environment has literally "come in from the cold." Yet this historic achievement is about more than the mysteries of the Arctic. It is also a lesson about the possibilities for progress that unfold when Americans and Russians join as partners in the peaceful service of our planet. Though we do not yet know precisely what truths the once forbidden information will reveal about the Arctic and our world, we do know that a great portal of knowledge has swung open and that we are passing through it as explorers together.

— AL GORE
Vice President of the United States

AUGUST 1961 Flying the Soviet flag, the nuclear icebreaker *Lenin* (foreground) plows north, trailed by the icebreaker *Yermak*. Borne by such vessels and by aircraft, the Soviets probed the Arctic Ocean for decades, seeking military advantage in the Cold War and amassing vast stores of environmental data. Information derived from this archive is now being made public, along with rare photographs of the Russian scientists at work.

GENNADY KOPOSOV

SEPTEMBER 1993 In private talks, Vice President Al Gore and Russian Prime Minister Viktor Chernomyrdin forged the political alliance that led to the exchange. "We built a relationship of trust," says Gore. "We each had to be sure that our national security would not be compromised."

By DON BELT ASSISTANT EDITOR

O N AN ICE FLOE 265 nautical miles north of Greenland, a dozen large men in parkas were doing their best to keep their sense of humor. They'd been standing around for an hour, which wouldn't have been so bad except for the wind, which was now gusting to 20 or 30 knots, and the windchill, which was down around 80 below. It was a clear morning in April, the month of perpetual daybreak in the high Arctic, when the sun hangs low in the sky like a frozen fruit, beautiful to look at but not much good.

As the men milled about to stay warm, they glanced anxiously at a 15-foot X carved in the flat snow nearby. Where the snow was cleared away, they could see a layer of thin white ice underneath—all that separated them from the abyssal depths of the Arctic Ocean. After looking it over, the men backed away and went back to milling.

Suddenly the X erupted with a colossal subaquatic roar, thrusting upward into a conical mountain of ice and snow. Chunks of ice tumbled away to reveal a block of metal rising from the sea—the dark gray conning tower of a nuclear submarine. Billows of steam poured out as the hatch was opened. Sailors in shirtsleeves materialized in the mist.

"Morning!" one called out to the men on the floe. "U.S. Navy, at your service!"

At least one observer was deeply impressed by the U.S.S. *Pargo*'s dramatic arrival. "To see that sub crash through the ice was absolutely amazing," recalls Vice President Al Gore, one of the men in parkas that day. "It was like the meeting of two worlds."

Bringing two worlds together—the world of environmental science and the world of national defense—would eventually produce the joint United States-Russian oceanographic atlas that Vice President Gore announces in the preceding pages. But in the spring of 1991, when Gore, then a U.S. senator, and several

MAY 1937 Arctic pioneers, members of the U.S.S.R.'s first scientific expedition to the North Pole, SP-1, lived for nine months on a drifting ice floe. Led by Ivan Papanin (second from right), the voyage proved that men on a drift station could collect mountains of data—and live to tell about it.

colleagues flew to the Arctic and boarded the *Pargo,* all this was just one crazy idea.

A longtime environmentalist, Gore had studied national security issues while serving on congressional intelligence and armed services committees. Along the way he became aware of the vast quantities of scientific data collected secretly by the U.S. intelligence community and the military that could also be applied to solving environmental dilemmas—rain forest decline, global warming, ocean pollution, desertification. Once convinced that sensitive material related to national security could be digitally excised from these data, Gore was determined to see much of the rest made available to science.

This is what propelled him to the Arctic in 1991 and placed him aboard the *Pargo,* which, after taking on its civilian passengers, sank back under the ice and set a course for the North Pole.

One of *Pargo*'s tasks was to test an array of instruments designed to gauge the thickness of polar ice from below. Gore was keenly interested in how data collected from these devices might be used to study global climate change: If the earth is warming, the theory goes, then the ice cube at the top of the world should be getting thinner.

Historically, of course, the U.S. Navy's interest in polar ice had nothing to do with global warming. During the Cold War both U.S. and Soviet strategists had regarded the Arctic as a potential staging area for World War III, which would probably have featured Soviet Typhoon-class submarines punching up through the ice to fire ballistic missiles at targets on land, and U.S. subs tracking their movements. Knowing how to find thin ice would be a strategic advantage in such a war. So would knowing all you could about the Arctic Ocean's weather—as well as its bottom topography, currents, and temperature and salinity, all of which affect acoustics.

The polar ice also provides ideal cover for prowling submarines, which could avoid

An Arctic Breakthrough

AUGUST 1966 Numbing cold and a coat of ice were all part of the job for sailors aboard the *Moskva,* a Soviet icebreaker plying Arctic waters for military, scientific, and commercial purposes. With some 3,000 miles of coastline on the Arctic Ocean — and its submarine fleet, based in

Murmansk, poised to wage nuclear war from under polar ice — the Soviet Union paid close attention to the icy waters on its doorstep. On the front lines: scientists from the Arctic and Antarctic Research Institute (AARI) in Leningrad, who fanned out to study the Arctic Ocean from top to bottom.

41

detection by maneuvering among the lobes and caverns on the ice's underside, where sonar is scattered and absorbed, making it much less effective.

After *Pargo* reached 90° north, the commander brought the sub to the surface as he had earlier, ramming up through thin ice. Gore climbed out and got his first look at the North Pole. "It was very bright—and the eeriness of the landscape was striking," he recalls. "Clouds of ice crystals were being blown back and forth by the wind, and I'll never forget how the ice sparkled in the air. It was a stunning experience."

SOME 500 MILES SOUTH of where Gore stood, a group of tired Russian scientists had, just days earlier, been weighing their chances of staying dry a few more hours. Riding a huge ice floe, Vladimir Sokolov had his doubts. "Pools of standing water," he recalls, "cracks in the ice. That sinking feeling." Evidence, in other words, that the ice platform was finally, after three and a half years of faithful service to the Soviet Union, breaking apart, softened by the spring thaw and crushed by the surrounding ice.

Since October 1987 dozens of scientists had lived and worked on this cake of ice, meticulously collecting oceanographic readings, weather observations, and ice data as the floe made a slow tour of the Arctic Ocean, pushed by winds and currents.

By April 1990, when Sokolov arrived by air to take command, the floe had turned south into the Canada Basin and stalled out. A few days later the drift station ran into what Sokolov calls an ice "meat grinder," a pressure system that grinds the ice floe to pieces as it rotates helplessly, held fast on all sides by thicker ice. "This is when the trouble started," Sokolov says—when the ice started to crack, when supply planes couldn't land without falling into a crevice, when his scientists were intermittently forced to stop taking measurements and start moving buildings from place to place in search of stable ice.

This went on for a year. Then things deteriorated further, although Sokolov's crew continued to collect data until the bitter end. They were finally evacuated by an Antonov cargo plane in April 1991. Dramatic endings were not at all unusual for drift stations in Arctic waters. In fact, Sokolov's expedition, known as SP-30 for *Severnyy Polyus* (North Pole),

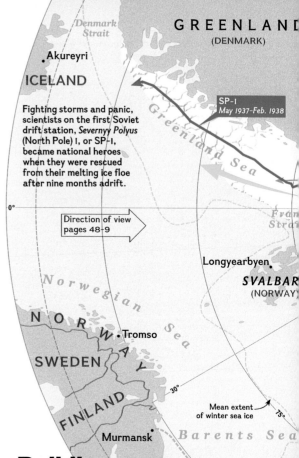

Fighting storms and panic, scientists on the first Soviet drift station, *Severnyy Polyus* (North Pole) I, or SP-I, became national heroes when they were rescued from their melting ice floe after nine months adrift.

Building a sea of knowledge

Storm-swept and locked in ice, the Arctic Ocean defied scientists long after other seas were being explored. Even the constant movement of Arctic ice went unexamined until 1893, when Norwegian explorer Fridtjof Nansen drove his research vessel, the *Fram*, into the ice pack and allowed it to freeze. Driven by wind and currents, the icebound *Fram* drifted some 2,200 miles in three years.

Taking a cue from Nansen, the U.S.S.R. in 1937 mounted the first of 31 drift stations— vanguard of a program for scientific and military research that grew to include more than a hundred polar stations, a dozen ships, and vast airborne surveys. Most activity ceased with the collapse of the U.S.S.R. in 1991.

During the Cold War, Western nations tried to keep pace with ice stations of their own, along with automated buoys and a massive reconnaissance effort from submarines, aircraft, and satellites. Inset maps (right) show the relative concentrations of observation points since World War II.

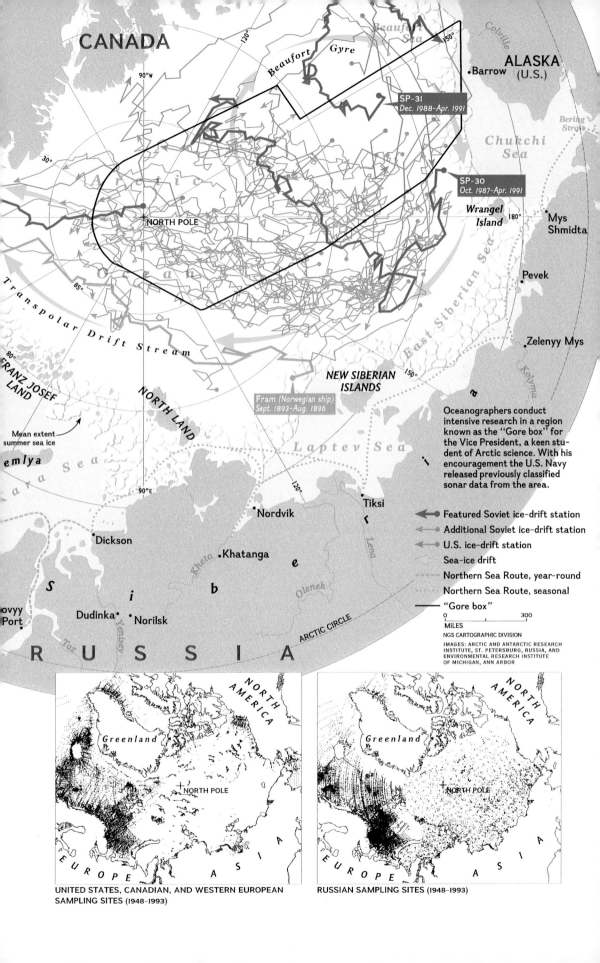

CANADA

Beaufort Sea

Beaufort Gyre

ALASKA
(U.S.)

• Barrow

120°

150°

Colville

SP-31
Dec. 1988-Apr. 1991

90°W

Chukchi
Sea

Bering
Strait

Arctic

30°

NORTH POLE

85°

SP-30
Oct. 1987-Apr. 1991

Wrangel
Island

180°

• Mys
Shmidta

Ocean

Transpolar Drift Stream

Pevek

Zelenyy Mys

East Siberian Sea

FRANZ JOSEF LAND

90°

NORTH LAND

150°

Kolyma

NEW SIBERIAN
ISLANDS

Fram (Norwegian ship)
Sept. 1893-Aug. 1896

Laptev Sea

Oceanographers conduct
intensive research in a region
known as the "Gore box" for
the Vice President, a keen student of Arctic science. With his
encouragement the U.S. Navy
released previously classified
sonar data from the area.

emlya

Mean extent
summer sea ice

Kara Sea

90°E

Nordvik

Tiksi

Lena

• Dickson

• Khatanga

Kheta

e

Olenek

S

i

b

← Featured Soviet ice-drift station

← Additional Soviet ice-drift station

← U.S. ice-drift station

Sea-ice drift

······ Northern Sea Route, year-round

······ Northern Sea Route, seasonal

—— "Gore box"

ovyy
Port

Dudinka •

• Norilsk

Taz

Yenisey

RUSSIA

ARCTIC CIRCLE

0   300
MILES
NGS CARTOGRAPHIC DIVISION

IMAGES: ARCTIC AND ANTARCTIC RESEARCH
INSTITUTE, ST. PETERSBURG, RUSSIA, AND
ENVIRONMENTAL RESEARCH INSTITUTE
OF MICHIGAN, ANN ARBOR

NORTH
AMERICA

Greenland

+ NORTH POLE

EUROPE   ASIA

UNITED STATES, CANADIAN, AND WESTERN EUROPEAN
SAMPLING SITES (1948-1993)

NORTH
AMERICA

Greenland

+ NORTH POLE

EUROPE   ASIA

RUSSIAN SAMPLING SITES (1948-1993)

was judged a rousing success, as was another ice station, SP-31, drifting near the Alaska coast that spring. No one knew it at the time, but SP-31 would be the last Soviet drift station in history.

FOR DECADES the Soviets had been tireless in their pursuit of knowledge about the Arctic. Part of the reason was military, of course: Sokolov's oceanographic data, like that from all drift stations, were considered vital for the fleet of Soviet submarines operating in Arctic waters from Murmansk and other ports. But the Soviets also had important economic and scientific reasons to be up there. Some 300 ships a year plied the Northern Sea Route along Russia's 3,000-mile Arctic coast. Navigators needed to know exactly where the ice was and its condition; scientists sought to understand its structure and movement. Besides launching one or two drift stations a year, the Soviets flew hundreds of missions to various parts of the Arctic, usually landing on skis, then collecting data on the ice or boring through it to sample the ocean.

These activities were run from the Arctic and Antarctic Research Institute (AARI) in Leningrad (now St. Petersburg), a bustling research center and staging area where patriotism ran high and money was no object. "Those were the days when no one asked, 'How much will it cost?'" remembers Leo Timokhov, a senior scientist at AARI and a man who has flown hundreds of sorties to the polar ice. "They would just say, 'Do it!'"

This era had begun 54 years earlier, when the Soviet Union had organized its very first drift station. Launched on May 21, 1937, near the North Pole, SP-1 was manned by a radio operator, hydrologist, magnetician, and the group's leader, a round, jovial member of the Soviet secret police named Ivan Papanin.

Outfitted in fur and housed in a canvas tent insulated with eiderdown, the four men trooped daily to the tents and wooden sheds where they conducted their research. They routinely lowered a cable to gauge the depth of the ocean and sampled sediment from its bottom. They also recorded water temperature at various depths, logged gravitational and magnetic readings, measured snow depth, analyzed the ice, and studied the weather.

As was the Russian practice, every observation was recorded twice—once in the hasty, semifrozen scrawl of the field notebook, and a

△ **JUNE 1987**
Along the ice's southern rim, melt pools develop as ice recedes during the summer, allowing navigation to resume on Russia's Northern Sea Route. Lifeline of the Russian Arctic, this 3,500-mile shipping corridor hugs the coast from Murmansk to the Bering Strait.

▷ **AUGUST 1966**
Left out in the cold after leaving the factory, a truck from a Gorki auto plant is hoisted off a cargo ship at Pevek, a port on the Northern Sea Route. As they have done since AARI's founding in 1920, scientists still monitor ice conditions for shipping, along with other aspects of the Arctic Ocean.

ALEXANDER KORNILOV (ABOVE); GENNADY KOPOSOV

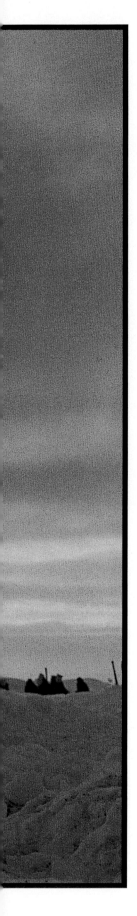

OCTOBER 1961
Blasting apart massive blocks of ice with explosives — and smoothing things over with bulldozers — engineers on a drift station typically built a runway first so that supply planes could land. Next they set up living quarters, mounted on sledges for mobility. Finally, they would assemble scientific equipment, like the stationary weather monitor (above) designed to transmit readings to AARI headquarters.

second time around the stove at night in the precise pencil notation that would make up the official record of the expedition. These paper notebooks would be stored at AARI and made available not only to the military but also to civilian Soviet scientists.

All went well during the summer and fall as the floe drifted south in a lazy zigzag pattern, driven by currents and prevailing winds. But by December their ice island had entered the Fram Strait east of Greenland and begun moving rapidly south, pelted by storms and chewed at by turbulent, ice-covered seas.

By February the four were up to their ankles in seawater. Arriving in the nick of time, a Soviet icebreaker plucked them from the ice — a rescue that caused a national sensation. Papanin and his mates were made Heroes of the Soviet Union and given a tumultuous ticker-tape parade through the streets of Moscow.

No such festivities awaited the drifters of SP-30 on their return to the motherland in April 1991. The mood in Moscow, indeed in the whole U.S.S.R., was a dark mixture of fatalism, anger, and fear. By December the Union of Soviet *(Continued on page 52)*

47

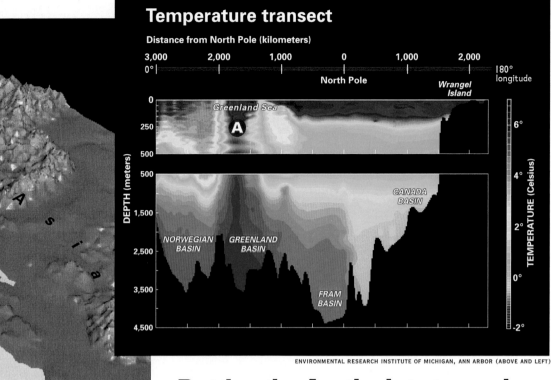

Temperature transect

Distance from North Pole (kilometers)

| 3,000 | 2,000 | 1,000 | 0 | 1,000 | 2,000 |

0° — North Pole — 180° longitude

Wrangel Island

Greenland Sea — **A**

DEPTH (meters): 0, 250, 500, 500, 1,500, 2,500, 3,500, 4,500

CANADA BASIN

NORWEGIAN BASIN GREENLAND BASIN

FRAM BASIN

TEMPERATURE (Celsius): 6°, 4°, 2°, 0°, -2°

ENVIRONMENTAL RESEARCH INSTITUTE OF MICHIGAN, ANN ARBOR (ABOVE AND LEFT)

Putting the Arctic data to work

The best model yet of Arctic Ocean temperature appears on the oceanographic CD-ROM in a cross section (above) combining U.S. and Russian data. Representing a transect of Arctic waters (red line, at left), the cross section shows an area of vertical mixing in the Greenland gyre (A), where warmer surface water is pulled in and cooled, forming a mass of deep ocean water. This column of cold water was previously known to Western science— but the Russians had been observing it methodically since the 1930s. Their data confirm that this is a long-term, fluctuating phenomenon. The data also are helping scientists draw a more accurate picture of how heat is exchanged between surface waters and the deep ocean and how warm and cold currents (below) affect global climate.

"That's the great thing about this CD-ROM," says NOAA Administrator D. James Baker. "It features a continuous set of measurements over time."

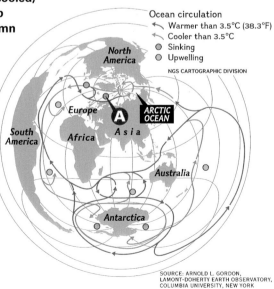

Ocean circulation
- Warmer than 3.5°C (38.3°F)
- Cooler than 3.5°C
- Sinking
- Upwelling

NGS CARTOGRAPHIC DIVISION

North America

Europe

South America

Africa

Asia

ARCTIC OCEAN

Australia

Antarctica

SOURCE: ARNOLD L. GORDON, LAMONT-DOHERTY EARTH OBSERVATORY, COLUMBIA UNIVERSITY, NEW YORK

ARCTIC AND ANTARCTIC MUSEUM (ALL)

△ **APRIL 1955**
Rolling out the bull-
dozers—essential
equipment for any
drift station—Soviet
scientists unload
cargo from a supply
plane. After a hiatus in
World War II, the Sovi-
ets swarmed over the
Arctic during the Cold
War, launching hun-
dreds of missions be-
tween 1950 and 1991.

◁ **JANUARY 1989**
Making snowballs for
science, ice physicist
Victor Morosov of
AARI uses an ice press
to study the snow on
drift station SP-28, as
colleagues use a drill
to test ice thickness.
Although the first
CD-ROM atlas from
the Gore-Chernomyr-
din Commission is
composed of oceano-
graphic data, a sub-
sequent atlas will
contain ice data from
drift stations and spy
satellites.

◁ **JUNE 1974**
Probing under the
ice, oceanographer
Gennady Kadachigov
moves among forma-
tions typical of the
Arctic Ocean. As very
cold, dense brine
seeps down from the
ice, the surrounding
seawater is cooled
and freezes to form
these stalactites. This
bizarre icescape had
strategic value dur-
ing the Cold War:
Because sonar is of
limited use in such
conditions, both U.S.
and Soviet subma-
rines could generally
avoid detection.

Socialist Republics would be history. The world, in short, was spinning like an ice floe caught in a meat grinder.

A FEISTY, FORTYISH WOMAN named Linda Zall was the person assigned to handle the letter that arrived at CIA headquarters in May 1990 from Senator Al Gore of Tennessee. Today, almost seven years later, she can still recite passages from it, like the last sentence on page one. "Gore wanted to know," she says, "if we had data related to 'sea surface temperature, sea ice type and motion, sea level data, ocean carbon dioxide, ocean chlorophyll, circulation patterns . . . trace species, cloud amounts, types and heights, precipitation, tropical winds, etc.'

"My first reaction when I read that sentence was, 'Why me, God?' " she says. "It was the 'etc.' that really worried me."

After the shock wore off, Zall set to work dissecting the letter "sentence by sentence, word by word" to see what complying with Gore's request might entail. The more she learned about the environmental data the CIA had in its "black," or secret, files, the more merit she saw in Gore's idea of releasing them. "But never in a million years," she says, "did I believe the agency would sign off on it."

Even with its old adversary faltering, the CIA was still a product of its long struggle against the U.S.S.R. "Remember," says Zall, "1990 wasn't like now, where we're sort of hugsy-kissy with the Russians. Most of the old guys at the CIA and in the Navy had spent their whole careers fighting the evil empire. The last thing they wanted was to open the black door, even a tiny crack."

Gore didn't know it yet, but in Zall he'd found someone at the CIA as relentless as he was. Early on she'd won permission to go outside the agency and meet privately with scientists to learn how intelligence data might apply to their work. Zall pursued dozens of the top scientists in their fields—figures such as oceanographer Walter Munk, geophysicist Gordon MacDonald, planetary physicist Michael McElroy, and polar climatologist Norbert Untersteiner of the University of Washington—all of whom donated their time and effort to studying Gore's request.

Then, in November 1991, Robert Gates became the director of the CIA. Gates, a long-time analyst, realized that the agency needed to redefine its mission in the post-Cold War world. A few weeks into his job Gates received a letter from Al Gore asking him to grant high-level security clearances to the scientists Zall had recruited, allowing them to study the most sensitive material in the files at the CIA and the Department of Defense.

Seeing an opportunity to make the CIA more "renaissance," Gates agreed. That summer Zall went into overdrive and got her group of 60 or so scientists top-secret clearances in record time. Their background checks went smoothly, although Zall nearly keeled over when she heard what Untersteiner, a high-spirited Austrian who'd been of draft age in 1944, answered when asked: "Have you ever been a member of an organization dedicated to the overthrow of the United States?"

"Yes," he wrote on the questionnaire, "the German army."

In a moment of pique Zall named her group of headstrong scientists Medea, after the character in Greek mythology who didn't let anything—even her children—stand in her way.

G ORE WAS INAUGURATED Vice President of the United States in January 1993. By then the Medea team had hit its stride, sifting through the billions of dollars' worth of classified material gathered by U.S. satellites, aircraft, ships, submarines, buoys, and other devices. This was a bonanza beyond imagining for earth scientists, and Medea's work— shepherded by Linda Zall—would ultimately lead to the release of military historical data, including spy satellite images, and a partial redeployment of the nation's satellites to help monitor the environment.

In April 1993 U.S. President Bill Clinton and Russian President Boris Yeltsin put Gore and Prime Minister Viktor Chernomyrdin in charge of a joint U.S.-Russian commission to foster initiatives for the good of both nations. Six months later Gore quietly raised the idea of sharing material from the intelligence archives of both nations for the good of the global environment. Chernomyrdin was receptive, says Gore, but "properly apprehensive" that Russia's national security not be compromised.

Months of painstaking negotiation followed, as the two sides grappled with the fine points of how to share national security information. "We had to figure out how to give up the milk without giving away the cows," says Victor Danilov-Danilian, Russia's Minister of the Environment.

FEBRUARY 1989   How to bathe on a block of floating ice? Russian scientists, like these on drift station SP-30, baked in a makeshift sauna, then dashed outside and rubbed their bodies with snow. Adrift for months at a time, Western and Russian ice camps were hotbeds of improvisation.

The two nations forged an Environmental Working Group, headed by Danilov-Danilian and NOAA Administrator D. James Baker of the United States, and the milk began to flow. The working group's initiatives range from analyzing environmental degradation at military facilities in both countries, to predicting earthquakes and other natural disasters, to assessing the impact of oil and gas development in permafrost regions.

The most dramatic progress so far has been in Arctic Ocean research, where shared data has led to a series of CD-ROM atlases. The first of these, released this month, is the most comprehensive collection of Arctic oceanographic data ever produced. About 70 percent of the data is derived from the Russian archive at AARI in St. Petersburg, while the rest comes from previously restricted international studies, the U.S. Navy, and the National Oceanic and Atmospheric Administration (NOAA). The Russian contribution, which consists of some 1.4 million winter observations, represents decades of toil by scientists

on both the airborne surveys and the drift stations—material drawn from 900,000 pages of documents that took 15 employees more than a year to transcribe. Subsequent atlases are being prepared on Arctic ice and meteorology.

Like many Russian scientific institutes, AARI is financially strapped. Its headquarters, including the library where the original data are shelved, is literally falling apart. Leo Timokhov, AARI's lead scientist on the project, says he and others breathed a sigh of relief when their notebooks were safely digitized and added to the CD-ROM. "It makes me very happy to see our data secure," says Timokhov, glancing at the cracked plaster over his head. "One never knows when a pipe will burst." He agrees with his colleagues in the U.S. that some of the most valuable oceanographic data in history have just been rescued.

It's too early to say what conclusions science will draw from this wealth of new information—but scientists, especially those studying long-term changes in the global environment, are eager to get their hands on it.

▷ **1950**
Among the dangers of life on the ice: polar bears, like the pair that were shot after menacing this drift station. The Soviets kept dogs to warn of a bear's approach. Most other hazards were related to weather. A man could survive blizzards and frost-bite, only to fall through ice weakened by storms or warm weather.

◁ **DECEMBER 1972**
Working the night shift—which lasts all winter—the crew of a weather station race through a blizzard to their barracks. A typical January entry in the diary of Ivan Papanin on SP-1: "The snowstorm rages unabated . . . we felt our ice floe quake again . . . hearts begin to palpitate. Our run-down condition is telling on us."

▽ **JANUARY 1958**
To fend off the effects of winter, a doctor gives light therapy to a worker overcome by life in total darkness. As a rule, workers were evacuated after one winter—although some, like oceanologist Leo Timokhov, relished Arctic night: "On the ice you're close to the cosmos— as if you are sediment on the bottom of a tranquil black sea."

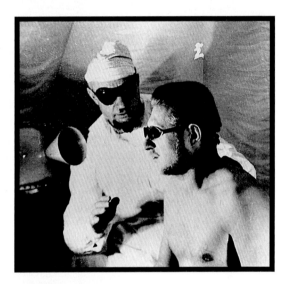

GENNADY KOPOSOV (ABOVE); ARCTIC AND ANTARCTIC MUSEUM

◁ **JANUARY 1955**
Ringing in the new, scientists at this drift station put up a traditional Russian New Year's tree and toasted their late premier, Joseph Stalin, who had died in 1953. Social gatherings were considered crucial to the success of a Soviet drift station. "We ate every single meal together," says one scientist. "It was a rule."

OCTOBER 1961 Scientists take a break from building the outpost where they would live for a year. "After one drift season we were friends for life," recalls Sergey Priamikov of AARI. "We were all in it together." Such thoughts today apply to nations. And as the Arctic CD-ROM shows, both the U.S. and Russia, in preparing for a war that might have destroyed the world, fashioned tools to help save it.

"This is, after all, the record of what's happened in the Arctic Ocean in the second half of the 20th century," says Norbert Untersteiner. "Throughout the Cold War the Russian Arctic was strictly off-limits to scientists from the West. This data changes all that. Now we'll know, for example, if the warm water anomaly we found in 1993 was there in 1970 or 1962 or 1950. It will allow us to paint the big picture in much greater detail."

Equally important, perhaps, is the principle behind the exchange. Everyone involved, both in the United States and Russia, believes that this kind of cooperation, when applied to the problems of global air pollution, say, or healing the acid-stressed boreal forest in Siberia, or containing nuclear and chemical wastes in the Arctic Ocean, is a source of genuine hope.

"The Russians want to understand the global environmental crisis just as much as we do," says Vice President Gore. "Solving it will be excruciatingly difficult; we both know that. It's at the outer boundary of what is possible to do as a civilization. But it *is* within our reach."

Victor Danilov-Danilian sees things from a different perspective. In his Moscow office, he sounded decidedly less upbeat. But even he brightened at the prospect of somehow turning the instruments of war into the means of environmental salvation.

"For us in Russia today," he said quietly, "this is one bright speck of paint on a very dark canvas." ☐

For further information on the Arctic Ocean Atlas CD-ROM visit the NOAA Web site at http://ns.noaa.gov/atlas, or contact User Services, National Snow and Ice Data Center (NSIDC), CIRES Campus Box 449, University of Colorado, Boulder, CO 80309-0449; (303) 492-6199, or e-mail NSIDC at nsidc_cd@ kryos.colorado.edu.

Lichens
More Than Meets the Eye

Often overlooked or ignored, symbiotic
organisms known as lichens, such as the
Xanthoria parietina dotting a Martha's
Vineyard farmhouse, are attracting new
attention for their medicinal, decorative,
and pollution-detecting properties.

By **SYLVIA DURAN SHARNOFF**

Photographs by the author and
STEPHEN SHARNOFF

Not plants, but . . .

For almost 25 years now my husband, Steve, and I have been captivated by the strange beauty and amazing diversity of lichens. Seven years ago our fascination drove us to photograph as many as we could of the 3,600 species in the United States and Canada. In pursuit of lichens we traveled from Alaska to the Florida Keys. We climbed trees, scaled cliffs, waded through swamps, crawled over tundra hummocks and desert sands—always hoping to find a lichen we hadn't seen before.

In the windswept valleys of eastern Idaho we found several. Ignoring the dramatic sagebrush country around me, I focused my attention on the ground, where yellowish almond-size lichens nestled amid the gravel (right). These were "vagrant" lichens, unattached and free to be blown about like tiny tumbleweeds. Collecting on snow-free ridges, they provide food for pronghorn during long, harsh winters. In the Middle East similar drifting vagrants were gathered by villagers and made into bread: the biblical "manna from heaven," some scholars believe.

A RESEARCH PROJECT SUPPORTED IN PART BY YOUR SOCIETY

Despite plantlike forms, lichens are not plants. Often called tiny ecosystems, they are actually compound organisms made up of two, or even three, very different partners, none of which is a plant. Biologists no longer find the concept of two great kingdoms—plants and animals—adequate for the classification of all living things. Fungi, bacteria, and simple organisms like algae now occupy kingdoms of their own. The dominant partner in the lichen symbiosis is a fungus, with a colony of algae or cyanobacteria—sometimes both—supplying food by photosynthesis.

Separated from its partners, the fungus itself would be a shapeless glob. In his studies of symbiosis in the 1970s, Vernon Ahmadjian teased apart *Cladonia cristatella* (right) into its fungal and algal components, which he cultured and then induced to recombine. Ahmadjian, of Clark University in Worcester, Massachusetts, was one of the first scientists to recombine lichens. His resynthesized lichen even produced the early stages of the red spore-bearing structures that give this species its common name, British soldiers.

This is the first appearance in the GEOGRAPHIC of the work of nature photographers SYLVIA and STEVE SHARNOFF.

Lichens to dye for

An arsenal of nearly 600 chemicals unique to lichens helps them survive in marginal environments and ward off attacks by bacteria, other fungi, and grazing herbivores. Called lichen substances, these pigments, toxins, and antibiotics have made lichens very useful to people in diverse cultures, especially as a source of dyes and medicines.

The warm browns in rugs made by members of the Ramah Navajo Weavers Association come from

boiling the vagrant lichen *Xanthoparmelia chlorochroa,* seen in a basket with a skein of dyed wool (left). The lichens once used to dye Scottish Harris Tweed contain substances that gave the fabric an earthy aroma and reputedly made it moth repellent. Shrubby gray lichens, scraped off Mediterranean coastal rocks and soaked in ammonia-rich stale urine, yielded some of the famous royal purple dyes of antiquity.

The most widely used dye lichen among Native Americans was the eye-catching wolf lichen *Letharia vulpina* (above right). The Chilkat Tlingit in Alaska traded coastal commodities such as fish oil for wolf lichen from the interior to color their prized dancing blankets, still worn by the Chilkat Dancers of Haines, Alaska, in their performances (top).

Though famed as a wolf poison, the wolf lichen often found a place in the Native American pharmacopoeia. The Okanagan-Colville, Blackfoot, and others made a medicinal tea from it or used it externally to treat skin problems. While scores of lichens have served as traditional medicines, few can compete with members of the genus *Usnea* (above left) as effective healers, used in teas and salves in nearly every part of the world. The lichen substance usnic acid has been used in some European antibiotic creams.

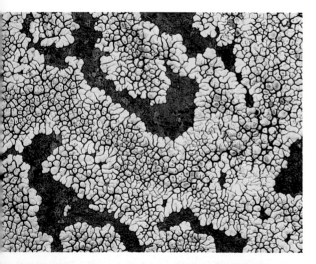

Designer rocks

As if painted by a mad hand, a slate outcrop is encrusted with lichens in the Sierra Nevada foothills of California (right). In western Nevada the Northern Paiute name for brightly colored crustose lichens used as medicines, such as *Pleopsidium oxytonum* (left), translates literally as "lizard semen," alluding to the push-ups that lizards do during courtship displays.

In legends of the Northwest's Interior Salish peoples, Coyote's long hair became entangled in a tree and was magically transformed into food, hanging from branches in thick clumps. Seen here interspersed with larch needles (bottom), *Bryoria fremontii* was a delicacy for some tribes and distasteful famine food for others. Some Interior Salish mixed the lichen with mud and used it for chinking log cabins. Others used it as fiber to make clothing. Northern flying squirrels build nests of it, which serve as cozy live-in larders, providing winter food. Anthropologist Craig Kirkpatrick of the University of California at Davis recently discovered that two other *Bryoria* species are the primary food of the endangered Yunnan snub-nosed monkey in China.

One of the most important of the so-called reindeer lichens, *Cladina stellaris* (center, among ground-hugging blueberries) is a favorite food of North American caribou and their Eurasian counterpart, reindeer. When the lichens are covered by snow, the animals dig craters as deep as three feet to reach them, fighting off competitors horning in for a free meal. Arctic peoples once ate reindeer lichens when times were rough, boiling them in water. They were considered a treat, however, when consumed, fermented, from caribou stomachs.

Colonizers

Almost any stable surface — like this gravestone on Cape Cod — makes suitable turf for lichens. Under favorable conditions, lichens will homestead on the stained-glass windows of cathedrals; on abandoned cars, highway signs, and roof shingles; even on the backs of Galápagos tortoises and beetles in New Guinea.

Growing imperceptibly for centuries — even millennia — some lichens are among the world's oldest living things. This makes them useful to scientists for dating archaeological artifacts and tracking geological events such as the retreat of glaciers.

Lichens help transform the landscape by slowly chipping away and dissolving rock into soil, adding organic matter when they die. In Israel's Negev desert, snails accelerate the process. Heavy dewfall there sustains lichens that grow under the surface of limestone rock, showing only their fruiting bodies. Snails grazing on the lichens scrape apart and ingest the rock, then excrete impressive amounts of soil.

Lichens in the U.S. Southwest form stable crusts that protect desert soils from erosion. Unfortunately, these crusts are very fragile, taking decades or longer to recover after being crushed by livestock or off-road vehicles.

Underfoot and overhead

Forest-floor carpet in British Columbia (left) includes a soil-enriching lichen, *Peltigera aphthosa,* and star-shaped mosses. The lichen contains bright green algae and is peppered with dark warts holding nitrogen-fixing cyanobacteria. The pale underside shows at the edges. Thriving in pristine environments, this species, like many other lichens, is fast disappearing in regions of air pollution and habitat disturbance.

Because of their extreme sensitivity, lichens are useful indicators of air quality. In Alaska, Forest Service scientists Chiska Derr and Linda Geiser (lower right, from left) compile data on lichen species in Tongass National Forest, which will be compared with future inventories to see how the lichens have fared. Lichens act like sponges, taking up pollutants that come their way. By analyzing lichens chemically, scientists can tell what's in the air.

Blown off trees in the Pacific Northwest during winter storms, witch's hair, *Alectoria sarmentosa* (top right), provides survival food for black-tailed deer. From the gondola of the Wind River Canopy Crane in Washington State, researchers study lichen growth patterns in treetops. Witch's hair becomes abundant only after trees are about a hundred years old.

Lichens: More Than Meets the Eye

Air monitors

After a winter rain, leafless trees in an Oregon farming valley come alive with lichens, including the oakmoss lichen, an important ingredient in many fine perfumes. Virtually dormant when dry, lichens become bright, plump, and metabolically active when damp.

Growing only where the air is very clean, *Usnea longissima* (right and with others at far right) was called pine gauze in a sixth-century Chinese herbal and is still used in traditional Chinese medicine. Locally abundant in the Pacific Northwest, it has all but disappeared in Europe.

Pollution is a serious threat to lichens even in the remote Arctic, and reindeer that rely on them for food are under increasing stress. In addition, fallout from the nuclear accident at Chornobyl contaminated lichens and thus reindeer in Scandinavia, where many herds had to be destroyed.

As early as 1859 European

scientists recorded that air pollution was killing lichens in urban and industrial areas. Today Steve and I note with growing concern that lichens are nearly absent from large areas, because the environment can no longer support this hardy yet vulnerable monitor of the very air we breathe. ☐

The First Steps

By RICK GORE
SENIOR ASSISTANT EDITOR

Photographs by KENNETH GARRETT

Art by RICHARD SCHLECHT

Few scientific fields stir debate as intensely as does the search for human ancestors. Strong emotions and deeply held religious beliefs crash against the physical evidence presented by paleoanthropologists. Some people do not accept the findings and interpretations of these scientists; rather they place humans on a family tree all their own, apart from other forms of life on earth. Others agree with the scientists who hold that evolution is a fact of life.

Even within the scientific community debates are passionate—not about whether the evolution from apelike creatures to humans took place but about the manner in which the long process occurred.

This report is one in a series on the dawn of humans that examines the most important discoveries from this contentious field and the meanings scientists draw from them. —THE EDITOR

Leaving tracks in rain-wet volcanic ash, primates crossed Tanzania's Laetoli plain 3.6 million years ago. Archaeologist Fiona Marshall and project leader Martha Demas discuss their team's efforts to conserve this unique record of our distant kin, who traveled around East Africa much as we do: side by side, upright and striding.

Bone collector

The Taung child skull is displayed with an image of a modern African crowned eagle, known to attack prey weighing as much as 40 pounds. These birds regularly kill primates, according to British biologist Steven Parry. New analysis of the skull—and the animal remains found with it—leads paleoanthropologists Lee Berger and Ron Clarke to reason that about 2.5 million years ago a similar raptor added this hominid skull to its refuse heap.

"**Y**OU WANT TO EAT what your ancestors ate?" Lee Berger, a bespectacled paleoanthropologist, is driving across the veld, or grasslands, of South Africa when he stops to ask this question. The ancestors he is talking about did not live last century, nor even within modern memory. They are early hominids— apelike creatures on the human family tree whose roots took hold more than four million years ago with the advent of bipedalism and who eventually evolved into us, *Homo sapiens.*

Without waiting for an answer, Berger opens his door and heads for a cluster of reddish brown termite mounds. A jackal howls in the distance, while zebras grazing nearby snort at our intrusion. Berger licks a long blade of grass and pokes it into a hole in one of the larger mounds. He pulls the blade out, laden with termites, and pops a few into his mouth.

"*Mmmm,* like herbs," he says, smiling. "They're good when you're really hot. They have all this acid in them, and it makes your mouth water. Try one."

I do. A crunch between the front teeth, a squirt, and an aftertaste I find more astringent than *mmmm.*

"Our ancestors would have eaten them, just as chimpanzees and some hunter-gatherers still do," he says. "They're pretty high in protein."

His eyes scan the grasslands around us.

"Do you realize how much food is out here—if you aren't picky?" he says, catching a grasshopper. "Have him. A bit gritty, but chockablock in nutrients." He rolls over a rock and grimaces at a centipede. "Don't eat that. It'll sting the heck out of you," he cautions before looking under another rock.

"If you really want to understand your ancestors, you've got to come to environments like this," he continues. "Just walking on the veld, they would have encountered all kinds of nutritious things—a field mouse or a bird's eggs or flying ants. And some of the roots and tubers out here make terrific food."

Trying to understand our ancestors has drawn me to South Africa. In the past decade a surge of hominid fossil discoveries, many of them made here, has electrified the science of human origins, intensifying debate about how a four-legged, tree-dwelling ancestor of humans, chimpanzees, and gorillas became a graceful runner who could race with lions on the savanna. For months I have been learning about the early hominids' first steps on the road to becoming human.

Paleoanthropologists love to draw hominid family trees. With the slightest encouragement—and sometimes without—many have grabbed my notebook and started sketching their own networks of branches winding from apes to modern humans. Details often differ, but most scientists agree that there have been two major groups, or genera, of hominids in the past four million years. One is our own genus, *Homo,* which appeared perhaps two and a half million years ago and which includes at least three species: *Homo habilis, Homo erectus,* and *Homo sapiens.*

One of the great mysteries of paleoanthropology is when, where, and how *Homo* replaced *Australopithecus,* the genus that inhabited much of Africa beginning around four million years ago. Australopithecines, as

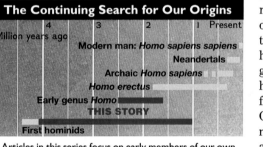

The Continuing Search for Our Origins

5 Million years ago	4	3	2	1	Present

Modern man: *Homo sapiens sapiens*
Neandertals
Archaic *Homo sapiens*
Homo erectus
Early genus *Homo*
THIS STORY
First hominids

Articles in this series focus on early members of our own genus and the hominids that preceded them. Much of this research was supported by your Society.

Hunger and fear

Predators on the ground and in the air threatened *Australopithecus africanus* three million years ago. With long, powerful arms and short legs, these small South African hominids may have sought cover among the branches. They foraged there too; *A. africanus* teeth show wear patterns similar to those found in modern primates that feed mainly on leaves and fruit.

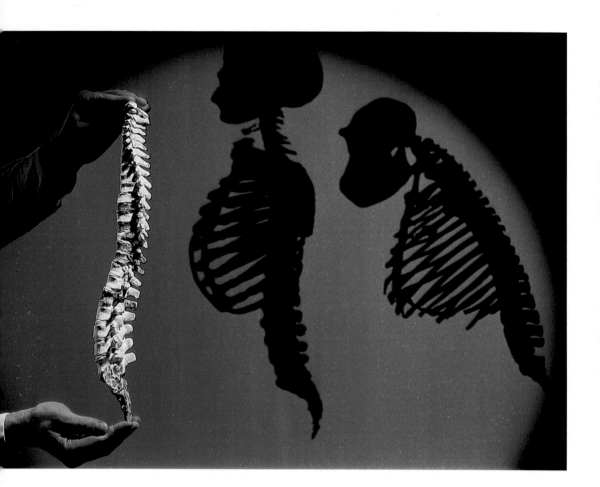

members of this genus are called, had apelike bodies and distinctly smaller brains than *Homo*, but they had mastered bipedalism, the hallmark of all hominids.

In 1925 anatomist Raymond Dart described the first australopithecine fossil, found in South Africa in a limestone cave called Taung. The fossil—a child's skull estimated to be 2.5 million years old—made international headlines. Dart noticed that the hole through which the child's spinal cord left the brain lay at the base of the skull, not toward the rear as in four-legged primates. To him that indicated that the child stood upright and walked on two legs—possibly the missing link between apes and humans. He named the new species *Australopithecus africanus*, which means "southern ape of Africa."

Older australopithecines have since been

KENNETH GARRETT's interest in ancient peoples dates back to his undergraduate years at the University of Virginia, where he majored in anthropology. Still a resident of Virginia, he has now photographed 15 articles for the GEOGRAPHIC.

found, and to date at least seven species have been identified. Several of those species are called robust australopithecines, because they had heavy features, including large jaws for crushing tough plant foods. The others also had relatively heavy jaws, but their overall build was lighter. The most famous representative of the gracefully built species is Lucy, a 3.18-million-year-old partial *Australopithecus afarensis* skeleton. When her remains were discovered by American paleoanthropologist Donald Johanson in 1974 at a site called Hadar in Ethiopia, Lucy became the oldest and most complete hominid known, and many scientists came to see her as the mother of humankind.

Most scientists agree that *afarensis* was crossing the line from ape to human. Like a chimpanzee, it had a small brain, long arms, short legs, and a cone-shaped thorax with a large belly. But *afarensis* stood upright and had made the breakthrough to bipedalism.

Until recently the most striking evidence of this shift to bipedalism lay buried beneath the remote acacia scrublands of northern

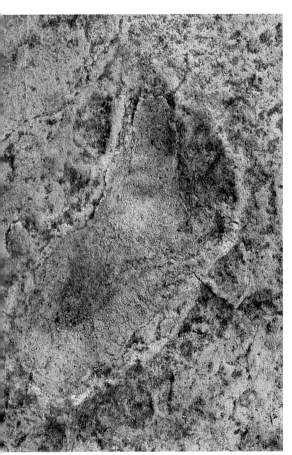

Built to walk

An obliging chimp shows off the splayed big toe typical of ape feet. More humanlike feet must have made the Laetoli tracks (detail, above), which show all toes parallel to the axis of the foot. The chimpanzee spinal silhouette (facing page, at right) exhibits the forward lean that makes four-limbed walking standard for the chimp. In modern humans, at center, spinal curves bring the pelvis, legs, and feet directly under the trunk, enabling two-legged travel. Anatomist Bruce Latimer has reconstructed an *Australopithecus afarensis* spine of about three million years ago, at left. The result matches human curves, supporting the contention that this species made the Laetoli tracks.

Tanzania. There, about 3.6 million years ago, a volcano called Sadiman erupted, blanketing the savanna with layers of ash. Shortly after the eruption at least two hominids walked across the ash, leaving their footprints behind. In 1978 a team led by the eminent paleoanthropologist Mary Leakey discovered and excavated those footprints.* Hoping to protect them from damage, the team buried the site with river sand a year later. But because the sand was filled with the seeds of acacia trees, a forest sprouted above the prints, threatening to destroy them with its roots. Alarmed Tanzanian officials, helped by the Getty Conservation Institute of Los Angeles,

California, launched an emergency operation in the summer of 1993 to kill the trees and excavate the tracks.

Sadiman volcano still lies on the horizon at Laetoli as I arrive at this desolate site on the edge of the Serengeti. I walk toward the white nylon canopy that covers the 30-foot-long excavation trench. Twenty-nine of the 69 prints have been exposed, and to everyone's relief the roots left the most important ones undamaged.

For years I have read of these buried tracks with no hope of ever seeing them. Suddenly they appear before me as if they were made

*See "Footprints in the Ashes of Time," by Mary D. Leakey, in the April 1979 NATIONAL GEOGRAPHIC.

last week by local Masai tribesmen walking through the gray mud of a water hole. I see two distinct trails. One was made by a small individual. The other track of slightly larger prints lies parallel about a foot away. Many scientists suspect that, like orangutans and gorillas, our earliest ancestors were sexually dimorphic— males grew much larger than females. Thus the first track may have been made by a female and the second by a male. And maybe not just one male. The imprint of a second big toe in several of the larger prints suggests that another individual may have walked in the footsteps of the first, like children do in the snow.

Staring out across the savanna, I imagine the scene. A hominid troop is sleeping in a grove of trees when the eruption awakens them. It is another in a series of explosions that has lasted for weeks. Members of the troop call to one another for comfort. The large males race to the ground to protect the females and young as a heavy snow of ash turns the landscape unfamiliar and frightening. Then, needing food, three apelike figures trudge across the land to forage.

The female was probably in the lead, says Bruce Latimer of the Cleveland Museum of Natural History, one of the anthropologists brought in by the Tanzanian government to study the excavated prints. While examining the prints, he saw that the female's track veered slightly; apparently she had sidestepped something on the ground. The first male made the same stutter step about a yard behind. Whether the third forager was in fact walking behind the others or came later is impossible to determine.

As I kneel beside the large print and lightly touch its sole, I am filled with quiet awe. It looks perfectly modern.

"I thought that at three and a half million years ago their prints might be somehow different from ours," says Latimer. "But they aren't. The bipedal adaptation of those hominids was full-blown."

But though this excavation has revealed new information, it has not solved the greatest mystery about the footprints: What kind of hominids made them? Latimer believes they were left by members of Lucy's species, *afarensis*. Although few of Lucy's foot bones have been found, the bones of other *afarensis* individuals from Hadar suggest to him that her foot could have fit the prints as easily as Cinderella's did the glass slipper. Other specialists dispute his interpretation, arguing that *afarensis* toes were too long and curved to make footprints as modern as those at Laetoli.

"Lucy was one of the stepsisters, not Cinderella," argues Russell Tuttle of the University of Chicago. He believes the tracks were made by a mystery hominid whose fossils have yet to be found.

SUCH DISAGREEMENT over bones is intense. I have often seen the faces of distinguished scientists flush as they've bashed one another's theories about the anatomy of *afarensis* with acerbic words. Those who hold that the species found at Hadar made the Laetoli footprints a thousand miles away and 400,000 years earlier believe this indicates that Lucy's species ranged across a great enough expanse of Africa for a long enough time to have given rise to *Homo*. Other scientists see a much more complex picture, arguing that many of the fossils we call *afarensis* may in fact be something else.

Some scientists are now even questioning Lucy's position as the mother of us all. Throwing out perhaps the greatest insult, Peter Schmid and Martin Häusler, anthropologists at the University of Zurich, recently proposed that Lucy might have been male.

This idea provokes exclamations of incredulity from Owen Lovejoy, the anatomist at Kent State University who painstakingly restored Lucy's pelvis, as well as from Donald Johanson, who discovered her skeleton. Both believe that *afarensis* was sexually dimorphic to a notable extent. "If Lucy is a male, imagine how small that would have made the females of her species," says Johanson.

In 1992 Johanson's team from the Institute of Human Origins in Berkeley, California, excavated a new *afarensis* skull at Hadar that is much larger than Lucy's, indicating that the individuals at Hadar did range enormously in size, perhaps according to sex.* Schmid, however, argues on the basis of his own reconstruction of Lucy's skeleton that "Lucy's pelvis has more male traits than female characteristics." For one, in his model Lucy—like modern males—lacks a ventral arc, a bony ridge on the front of the pubic bone, found in almost all modern females. Häusler adds that Lucy's pelvis is too small to have given birth to an australopithecine infant. "The only reason you

*See "Face-to-Face With Lucy's Family," by Donald C. Johanson, in the March 1996 issue.

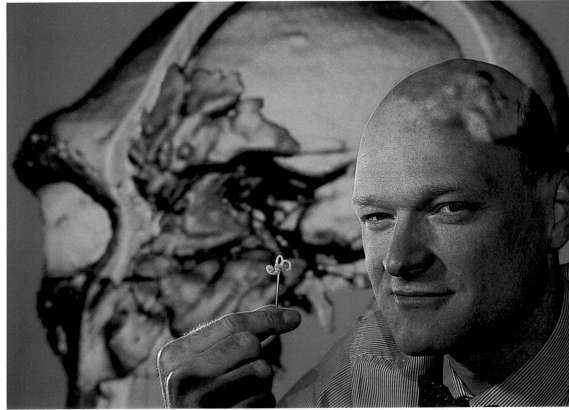

CT SCAN BY F. ZONNEVELD AND C. STRINGER

Balancing act

Images of sinus cavities (green) and a brain cavity (yellow) are based on CT scans of the skull of an archaic *Homo sapiens*. Anatomist Fred Spoor holds a cast of a modern human inner ear, which transmits balance information and sound signals to the brain. Using CT scans to compare the organ with similar structures in fossil skulls, Spoor studies how our forebears maintained their balance.

would say Lucy is a female is her small size," says Häusler. "Perhaps we should change her name to Lucifer."

Lori Hager, a paleoanthropologist at the University of California at Berkeley, agrees with Schmid that by modern human standards Lucy does not look clearly female, though Hager concedes that such a comparison may be pointless. Modern female pelvises are wider than those of modern males because as human brains expanded, women needed birth canals large enough to deliver large-brained infants. "You can't determine the sex of chimpanzees on the basis of their pelvises," Hager says. "Maybe there weren't pelvic differences in australopithecines either."

Hager and others believe that male and female australopithecines, like chimpanzees, were not noticeably different in appearance and that the variation in size is because there

were at least two species of australopithecines at Hadar—one large and one small. This hypothesis, if true, will strengthen an increasingly popular idea: Many species on the early hominid family tree remain to be found.

Meave Leakey, the noted Kenyan paleoanthropologist, recently found one of these species—an australopithecine older than *afarensis*. Because the 4.1-million-year-old fossils were discovered at Kanapoi, near modern Lake Turkana in northern Kenya, she calls her new australopithecine *anamensis*, which means "of the lake" in the local Turkana language.*

Tan and lanky, Meave Leakey is continuing the work she helped her husband, Richard, pioneer in the 1970s. I meet her at the National Museums of Kenya (Continued on page 88)

*See "The Farthest Horizon," by Meave Leakey, September 1995.

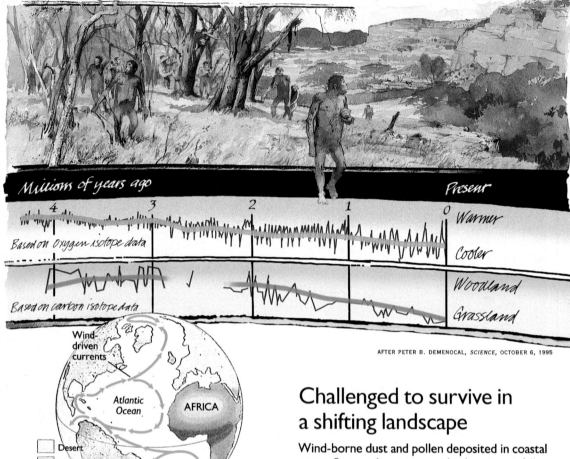

Millions of years ago   Present

4   3   2   1   0   Warmer

Based on oxygen isotope data   Cooler

Based on carbon isotope data   Woodland

                                                                     Grassland

AFTER PETER B. DEMENOCAL, *SCIENCE*, OCTOBER 6, 1995

Wind-driven currents

Atlantic Ocean   AFRICA

☐ Desert
☐ Savanna and scrub
☐ Transitional woodland
■ Rain forest

ANCIENT GLOBAL CLIMATE
Before 3.5 million years ago Atlantic and Pacific waters mix in the open passage between the Americas, balancing salinity levels. Buoyant Atlantic currents temper the chill of the Arctic Ocean.

Ice cap

Sinking North Atlantic Current

Atlantic Ocean   AFRICA

Wind-driven currents

MODERN GLOBAL CLIMATE
The Pacific no longer mixes with west-moving Atlantic waters in the tropics. The North Atlantic Current, heavy with salt, sinks before it reaches the polar sea. Deprived of warmth, the Arctic freezes, ultimately causing a cooling, drying effect in Africa.

Challenged to survive in a shifting landscape

Wind-borne dust and pollen deposited in coastal ocean-floor sediments provide clues to rainfall, temperature, and vegetation patterns in Africa over nearly five million years (graph, above). Many scientists find significant correlations between periods of climate change and important junctures in hominid development.

Early hominids like the australopithecines illustrated above possessed features that helped them survive in a variety of landscapes. A biped's free hands are able to gather a broad range of foods. Erect posture offers less surface to absorb the sun's heat and exposes more skin to moving air, helping bipeds keep cool on the open plains.

According to geologist Steven Stanley, Africa grew cooler and drier after the Isthmus of Panama rose (globes, left). Rain forests shrank; woods were broken by broad stretches of grassland. Stanley believes this change drove the split between *Australopithecus* and *Homo*.

Paleoanthropologist Robert Blumenschine calls Tanzania's Ngorongoro Crater (right) "a modern analog" of an eastern African landscape that likely challenged hominids between one and two million years ago. Dense forest darkens the crater's southern rim, foreground. Downslope, open acacia woodland thins into savanna. Grasses and sedges ring a dry lake bed. In the distance a stream winds across the crater floor, and on the far rim trees thicken again.

A *Australopithecus anamensis*

MICHEL BRUNET

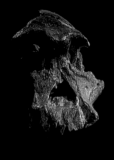

ENRICO
FERORELLI

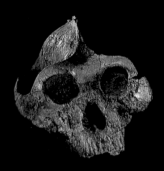

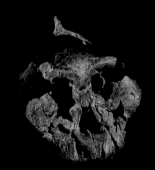

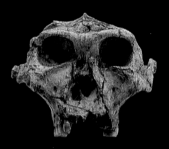

DAVID L. BRILL

B *Australopithecus bahrelghazali*

6 FEET

4.5 FEET

A. anamensis, oldest member of its genus, dates from around four million years ago. A. bahrelghazali jaw and teeth were found 1,500 miles west of the East African Rift.

C *Australopithecus afarensis*

Date range: 3.9 to 3 million years ago. Distribution: Eastern Africa. Features: Apelike arms, with spine, pelvis, and lower limbs suited for an upright stance and two-legged gait.

D *Australopithecus africanus*

Date range: 3 to 2.3 million years ago. Distribution: Southern Africa. Features: A higher, rounder braincase than *afarensis* but limbs possibly less adapted for bipedalism.

E *Australopithecus aethiopicus*

Date range: 2.6 to 2.2 million years ago. Distribution: Eastern Africa. Features: Massive chewing muscles anchored to a prominent bony crest along the top of the skull.

F *Australopithecus boisei*

Date range (including *A. aethiopicus**): 2.6 to 1 million years ago. Distribution: Eastern Africa. Features: Powerful upper body, tall upper jaw, largest molars of any hominid.

G *Australopithecus robustus*

Date range: 2 to 1.2 million years ago. Distribution: Southern Africa. Features: A flatter face, with more prominent cheeks and less protruding jaws than *afarensis* or *africanus*.

Limbs and branches on the family tree

These trees present conflicting interpretations of hominid history spanning nearly five million years. Phillip Tobias views *Homo* as a fairly simple genus descended from *A. africanus* two to three million years ago. Bernard Wood views *Homo* as a more complex genus with no clear path of descent from the australopithecines. They agree that robust australopithecines occupy a separate lineage that went extinct about one million years ago—but disagree on how many robust species existed. Such diagrams frame the current debate about our species' ancestry. Future fossil discoveries will test both.

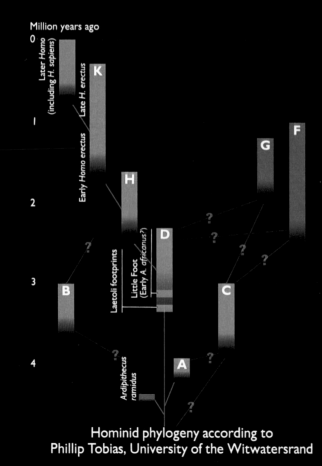

Hominid phylogeny according to
Phillip Tobias, University of the Witwatersrand

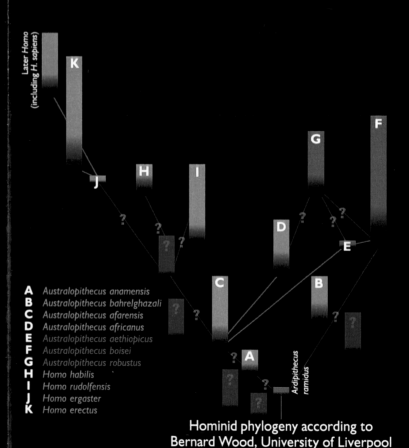

A Australopithecus anamensis
B Australopithecus bahrelghazali
C Australopithecus afarensis
D Australopithecus africanus
E Australopithecus aethiopicus
F Australopithecus boisei
G Australopithecus robustus
H Homo habilis
I Homo rudolfensis
J Homo ergaster
K Homo erectus

Hominid phylogeny according to
Bernard Wood, University of Liverpool

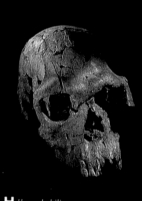

H *Homo habilis*

Date range (including *H. rudolfensis**): 2.5 to 1.6 million years ago. Distribution: Eastern and southern Africa. Features: Larger brain and smaller teeth than *Australopithecus*.

■ **Site or region name**
■ **Homo**
■ **Robust australopithecines**
■ **Australopithecines**
■ **Ardipithecus**

A F R I C A

SIDI ABDERRAHMAN
H. erectus

TIGHENIF
H. erectus

BAHR EL GHAZAL (KT12)
A. bahrelghazali

HADAR
Homo sp.?
A. afarensis

MIDDLE AWASH/ARAMIS
A. afarensis
Ardipithecus ramidus

OMO
H. erectus
H. habilis
H. rudolfensis
A. boisei
A. aethiopicus
A. afarensis

WEST TURKANA
H. erectus
A. boisei
A. aethiopicus
A. afarensis

8. KOOBI FORA
H. erectus
H. habilis
H. rudolfensis
A. boisei
A. afarensis

9. ALLIA BAY
A. anamensis

10. LOTHAGAM
A. afarensis

KANAPOI
A. anamensis

11. LAKE BARINGO
H. erectus
Homo sp.?
A. boisei

12. PENINJ
A. boisei

13. OLDUVAI GORGE
H. erectus
H. habilis
A. boisei

14. LAETOLI
A. afarensis

15. MALEMA
A. boisei

URAHA
H. rudolfensis

16. MAKAPANSGAT
A. africanus

17. KROMDRAAI
A. robustus

STERKFONTEIN
H. habilis
A. africanus

SWARTKRANS
H. habilis
A. robustus

18. TAUNG
A. africanus

0   750
MILES
NGS CARTOGRAPHIC DIVISION
IMAGE GENERATED BY ROBERT STACEY,
WORLDSAT INTERNATIONAL INC.

GENUS *HOMO*

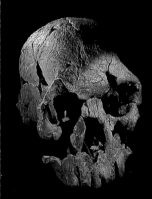

I *Homo rudolfensis*
Date range:
2.5 to 1.9 million
years ago.
Distribution:
Eastern Africa.
Features: A long,
broad face with
flatter brow-
ridges and a
larger, rounder
braincase than
habilis.

J *Homo ergaster*
Date range:
1.8 to 1.4 million
years ago.
Distribution:
Eastern Africa.
Features: Small-
er jaws and a
more projecting
nose than earlier
Homo; more
modern arm and
leg proportions.

K *Homo erectus* (not shown)

Remains of this diverse species are found in Asia as
well as in Africa. Its braincase was low and heavy, and
prominent browridges
shadowed the face. Stature
in males and females was
close to that of modern
humans. The earliest specimens—1.8 million years
old—sometimes classified
as *H. ergaster**, come from
eastern Africa. *Erectus* also
lived in Algeria, Morocco,
and South Africa. By one
million years ago *erectus*
occupied Java, Indonesia,
and China. Future articles in
this series will explore the
Homo erectus story in detail.

*Many researchers do
not regard *A. aethiopicus,*
H. rudolfensis, and *H. ergaster*
as separate species, combining
them instead with *A. boisei,*
H. habilis, and *H. erectus,*
respectively.

(Continued from page 81) in Nairobi, where she shows me pieces of *anamensis,* including a narrow, apelike mandible with small, vaguely human-looking teeth. She also has two ends of a tibia, the larger of the two lower leg bones. They are telltale fossils: The strength of the tibia and the angle at which it must have joined the knee and ankle indicate that *anamensis* walked on two legs half a million years—or 25,000 generations—earlier than the Laetoli hominids. Leakey's goal now is to explore more four-million-year-old sediments. Fossils of that age, she says, "will tell us more about the split between chimps and humans."

The next day we fly a small plane to a remote site called Allia Bay on the shore of Lake Turkana. Four million years ago this landscape was prime hominid habitat. A forest along a river's edge provided shelter and fruit, while nearby grasslands and patchy woodlands would also have been good for foraging. Beyond the landing strip there is no hint of civilization today. When we set down at 9:30 a.m., the temperature has already hit 97°F—by midday it will push 120°. Strong winds gusting off the lake constantly suck moisture from my body. "Drink, drink, drink. At least two gallons a day even if you don't feel thirsty," cautions Leakey.

At night hyenas whoop and lions roar, while deadly, pencil-thin carpet vipers lurk in the sand. I am assigned to the camp's only vacant tent—about a hundred yards from the others. While the relentless wind shakes my isolated shelter, I lie awake, alert to the slightest noise. Did our early ancestors face the night feeling so vulnerable? I don't imagine my ability to run on two legs would help much if a hungry carnivore appeared outside the tent. I try to remember where the nearest tree is.

Leakey and her longtime colleague, Alan Walker of Pennsylvania State University, seem oblivious to such concerns—a trait I find common to the sun-weathered men and women whose passion for finding ever older bones drives them to such punishing sites. Leakey can walk all day intently scanning the ground for scraps of bone under the withering winds and sun and return to camp seemingly recharged, exhilarated, and ready to handle such practical problems as getting fresh meat or repairing vehicles.

Over dinner we discuss the growing complexity of our view of human origins. Already many scientists are arguing that the tibia she found last year resembles *Homo* more than it does *afarensis.* They suggest that it might be part of another line of hominids, one that could have made the Laetoli footprints and later evolved into us. But Leakey thinks that her new bones and those of Lucy's species are similar enough, at least from the neck down, to make *anamensis* Lucy's direct ancestor. She sees differences, though, in the teeth and skull. "*Anamensis* had a more primitive, chimplike head than Lucy," she says. She suspects that her find is but one of many hominid species that evolved after the advent of bipedalism.

"I think *anamensis* may turn out to be just one twig on a bushy bush," she says. "Most of the other twigs may never be found, and it may never be possible to say exactly what evolved into what. What matters is what these animals were doing—experimenting with bipedalism. Why? What caused this breakthrough?"

TO THE NORTHEAST of Lake Turkana, in Ethiopia, a site called Aramis may soon help answer these questions. An international team including Tim White of Berkeley and his Ethiopian colleague, Berhane Asfaw, has been uncovering a 4.4-million-year-old species that White believes is the oldest hominid yet discovered. He thinks this new species is so different from *Australopithecus* that he has created an entirely new genus for it. Borrowing the word for "ground" in the local Afar language, he calls it *Ardipithecus,* or "ground ape." Its species name, *ramidus,* means "root."

"*Ramidus* is the first species this side of our common ancestor with chimpanzees," he says. "It's the link that's no longer missing."

Several of White's colleagues tell me they suspect *ramidus* actually belongs on the chimp lineage; its teeth look too primitive to be on the main line of human evolution. But, except for the teeth, few have seen the fossils, which White refuses to discuss in detail until he has thoroughly studied them. The key question, of course, is whether *ramidus* was bipedal.

White just smiles when I ask him that question in his lab in Berkeley's Life Sciences building. "Let's just say *ramidus* had a type of locomotion unlike anything living today," he finally says. "If you want to find something that walked like it did, you might try the bar in *Star Wars.*"

Fit and wiry, White brims with confidence. Few anatomists are as respected as he is for the

Brain space

Even the clever chimpanzee (right) seems small-brained next to a modern human (below right) in these images from a University of Zurich exhibit. The head of a baby chimp passes easily through the birth canal (diagram, below). In contrast, tremendous force is required to move a human infant's large head through its mother's narrow pelvis. Scientists speculate that *A. afarensis* females, such as Lucy, shared both conditions: They gave birth to small-headed infants, but the birth process was still difficult, because their pelvises were narrowed for upright posture.

AFTER ROBERT G. TAGUE AND C. OWEN LOVEJOY,
JOURNAL OF HUMAN EVOLUTION, MAY 1986

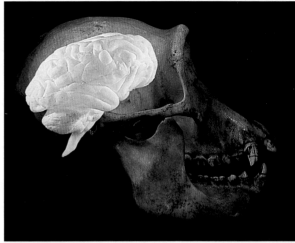

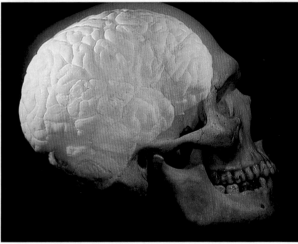

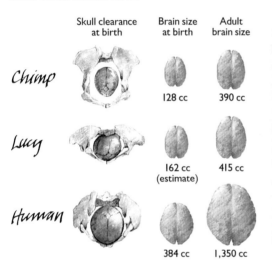

	Skull clearance at birth	Brain size at birth	Adult brain size
Chimp		128 cc	390 cc
Lucy		162 cc (estimate)	415 cc
Human		384 cc	1,350 cc

rigor of their analyses—and few are as feared for the sharpness of their criticism. Today he is ebullient. Aramis is the site of a lifetime.

"We spent last season crawling over the ground, looking for every piece of bone across sediments stretching six kilometers. We now have parts of more than 50 individuals," he says, adding that his group also collected more than a hundred pieces of a single skeleton, including a partial foot and seven out of eight wrist bones. "We have what will let us understand its hands and feet in a way we couldn't touch with Lucy," he says.

Besides *ramidus,* the Aramis site is turning up hundreds of bones of monkeys and spiral-horned antelope called kudu. Both animals are forest dwellers, suggesting that *ramidus* lived in thickly wooded habitats. This discovery is helping to overturn the traditional belief that bipedalism emerged on the open savanna.

Many scientists had thought that hominids began walking to adjust to a major climate change that, starting about six million years ago, dried out the primeval forests and forced them to forage in the open country. Some scientists now suspect that our ancestors began to develop bipedalism in the trees. They may have walked upright on large branches or collected fruit from overhead by standing on limbs while hanging with one arm onto higher ones. By the time the forests began to shrink, the forerunners of early hominids were probably bipedal at least part of the time.

Kevin Hunt of Indiana University has observed chimpanzees for hundreds of hours in Africa and thinks that, like them, the immediate ancestors of the hominids stood on two legs most often when they fed from the ground on the fruit of small trees. Trees like *Grewia,* which today grow in stands of as many as a

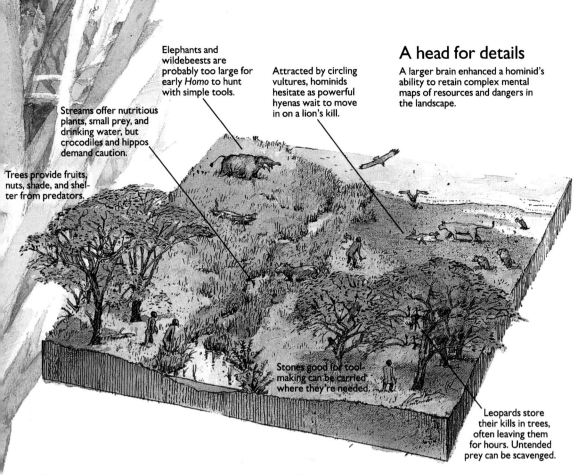

Elephants and wildebeests are probably too large for early *Homo* to hunt with simple tools.

Streams offer nutritious plants, small prey, and drinking water, but crocodiles and hippos demand caution.

Trees provide fruits, nuts, shade, and shelter from predators.

Attracted by circling vultures, hominids hesitate as powerful hyenas wait to move in on a lion's kill.

A head for details

A larger brain enhanced a hominid's ability to retain complex mental maps of resources and dangers in the landscape.

Stones good for toolmaking can be carried where they're needed.

Leopards store their kills in trees, often leaving them for hours. Untended prey can be scavenged.

Stepping-stones to change

Two million years ago early members of the genus *Homo* exhibited familiar human traits: increased brain size, toolmaking, and a high-quality diet. Each trait influenced the others' development. Even the simple technology of stone-tool production indicates increased mental abilities. Gathering workable stones, remembering flaking angles, and matching tools to tasks called for bigger brains than earlier species possessed. Australopithecine brain volume averaged 400 to 500 cubic centimeters (cc). Early *Homo* specimens show volumes of 600 to 750 cc.

As anthropologist Leslie Aiello notes, large brains are "expensive" organs, requiring high energy levels to operate (diagram, right). Human brains use about 20 percent of the body's total energy production. Fueling growth in such a demanding organ requires food dense with calories and nutrients. Early *Homo* appears to have added meat from larger animals (left) to the mainly herbivorous australopithecine diet. *Homo habilis* was a fairly small species, and its tool kit consisted mostly of fist-size hammerstones and small, sharp flakes. Many researchers believe that, with neither the stature nor the weapons of a mighty hunter, these early humans used their brains and tools for scavenging the prey of stronger, faster carnivores (above). Breaking open the bones of a single wildebeest's leg, filled with fatty marrow, an individual could consume half a day's calorie needs in one relatively safe and easy meal.

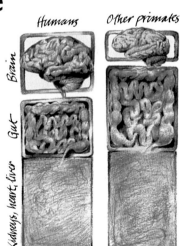

Humans   Other primates

Brain

Gut

Kidneys, heart, liver

Trade-off for a better brain

Increased brain capacity may have helped *Homo* secure a higher quality diet, which allowed for a smaller gut. As guts shrank, more energy became available to run a still larger, more complex brain.

AFTER LESLIE C. AIELLO AND PETER WHEELER, *CURRENT ANTHROPOLOGY*, APRIL 1995

hundred over an area the size of a typical city block, may have been common in a landscape shifting from forest to drier, open woodland.

"The pre-hominids were probably already more bipedal than chimps today," says Hunt. "As they were forced into areas of smaller trees like *Grewia,* it became more efficient for them to feed standing upright on the ground rather than trying to move through the branches from tree to tree."

Once on the ground, it would have taken less energy to shuffle on two legs from tree to tree than to raise the torso from a four-legged posture to feed, then lower it again to move on all fours to the next tree. "That would have had a side benefit," says Henry McHenry of the University of California at Davis. "It freed the hands to do other things."

As the amount of shady habitat shrank, keeping the brain cool might have been another factor in the development of bipedalism, says Peter Wheeler of Liverpool John Moores University. One way to reduce the risk of heatstroke is to stand upright. "During the most stressful part of the day a biped on the savanna gets only a third of the solar heat load a quadruped does," says Wheeler. Also, with more of the body exposed to cooling breezes, shedding heat becomes easier, requiring hominids to consume less water.

In the debate over why the first hominids developed bipedalism, Lucy takes center stage once again. While Owen Lovejoy of Kent State has long believed that Lucy lived exclusively on the ground, others think she was equally at home in the trees. *Afarensis,* they point out, would have been a good climber because of the mobility of its joints and its strong arms and shoulders. And because its long, curved fingers and toes would have helped it grasp branches.

Others question how efficient a biped Lucy really was. Peter Schmid, one of the Swiss anthropologists who challenged Lucy's gender and one of the specialists brought to Laetoli to study the footprints, says that his reconstruction of Lucy's skeleton suggests that she would have rotated her trunk when she walked, waddling like a gorilla.

Unlike modern humans, Schmid says, Lucy didn't have light ribs and a widening of the upper part of the thorax that would let her take in more oxygen and cool her body efficiently when she ran. He maintains that Lucy would have had to pant like a dog to cool herself.

Running any distance on the savanna would have caused heat exhaustion.

ARGUMENTS OVER early bipedal techniques flared after a discovery called Little Foot by Phillip Tobias and Ron Clarke of the University of the Witwatersrand in Johannesburg. A cluster of bones that made up the instep of a hominid that lived in southern Africa between 3 and 3.5 million years ago, Little Foot had for years lain misidentified in a drawer full of baboon fossils uncovered at Sterkfontein, one of South Africa's great fossil excavations. After Clarke recognized the bones as hominid in 1994, they were transferred to a felt-lined plastic box and stored in the vault at Tobias's laboratory.

"I love it with all my heart," Tobias says as he removes the pieces of Little Foot from the box and assembles them on his desk. "The big toe of this hominid deviated so it could swing out to the side as our thumbs can," he says, moving the toe bone back and forth. Modern humans can move the big toe up and down, but chimps have more range of movement, enabling them to grasp. But while Little Foot had that apelike feature, its ankle was more humanlike. "This combination suggests that our feet became human gradually," says Tobias, "from ankle to big toe."

When Little Foot wanted to, say Tobias and Clarke, it could have retracted that grasping big toe and walked much as we do, even though it retained tree-climbing skills. They even think that Little Foot was the kind of hominid that made the Laetoli footprints.

Scientists who believe that *afarensis* made the footprints have attacked Tobias and Clarke's interpretation. Whether or not their claim that Little Foot walked with a divergent big toe holds up, they have fanned a controversy. Some scientists now wonder whether hominids experimented with different ways of being bipedal.

During the 1980s, while South Africa was isolated from a world increasingly intolerant of apartheid, Sterkfontein produced hundreds of new *africanus* specimens, including many fossils from the arms, legs, torso, and pelvis— *africanus* body parts rarely found before. In 1994, with the end of apartheid, news of these discoveries began filtering out. Some of these finds may even turn out to be new species. Lee Berger, Tobias and Clarke's colleague at

The anatomy of dexterity

Hammerstones, like this one from Laetoli, are among the earliest human artifacts. Repeated blows left surface markings that distinguish them from naturally broken rocks. Early tool expert Nick Toth (above) has implanted wire sensors in his forearm and hand to measure muscle activity involved in various toolmaking techniques. An avid blues musician, Toth was curious to see the muscle-use patterns recorded during musicmaking, so he played his guitar while his hand was "plugged in."

Witwatersrand and my escort on the veld, thinks the unexpected traits of these fossils overturn the long-standing assumption that the genus *Homo* evolved in East Africa. He believes *Homo* emerged on the southern end of the continent and strode north.

From the same vault where Phillip Tobias keeps his Little Foot specimens, Berger pulls out one new fossil after another. Most of them date, he estimates, from around 2.6 million years ago. He shows me a knee joint whose surfaces indicate that *africanus* had a more bowlegged, apelike gait than Lucy, who many

believe gave rise to this southern cousin. How could Lucy evolve into something with a more primitive knee, he asks.

Berger proposes that bipedalism arose at least twice. He believes that the first bipeds evolved in East Africa, generating an initial group of hominids, including *afarensis*, that dead-ended by evolving into one of the robust forms of australopithecines. A second evolution, he argues, may have taken place later in southern Africa, parts of which he thinks remained forested longer and would have required South African hominids to maintain

the arboreal skills more common to apes.

But not every characteristic of *africanus* was primitive. Berger shows me a finger fragment that he says looks remarkably human. So does a mandible he takes out of the vault; its teeth are smaller than *afarensis'*, and the molars are of the same type and arrangement as *Homo*'s. Most surprising are cranial remains that suggest to Berger that some of these hominids had taken another step on the road to humanity. He believes that they had brains as large as those of early *Homo*.

Berger says the ancient ecology of southern Africa may have driven the increase in brain size of its hominids. Because the region may have had a more complex mosaic of habitats with a greater diversity of predators and food sources than East Africa, the challenges of surviving there might have required *africanus* to become smarter.

Some scientists believe that such environments further contributed to an expanding brain size by forcing hominids to create larger social groups. "Ecological challenges, outsmarting predators, defending resources all require bigger groups," says Robin Dunbar, an evolutionary psychologist at the University of Liverpool. With more relationships and pecking orders to keep track of, he says, hominids needed bigger brains.

Survival for any early hominid was no small challenge. Big cats probably posed the greatest threat, but Berger and Ron Clarke recently identified another predator and in the process may have solved a long-standing murder mystery: the death of the famous Taung child.

Berger brings out a small wooden box and opens it to reveal the three pieces of the Taung child—its jaw, its face, and a cast of its brain. "It's our crown jewel," he says, fitting the pieces together. Assembled, the skull is about the size of a large grapefruit. Its haunting eye sockets and full set of milk teeth mesmerize with the same sense of symmetry found in a great work of art. Turning the skull, Berger points out holes on the top of it. "No one has

Evolution headquarters

Even after decades of excavation at Olduvai Gorge (above), Rutgers University paleoanthropologist Robert Blumenschine says, "there's no end to the treasures that can be found." Louis and Mary Leakey's pioneering work established Olduvai as the most famous of early prehistoric sites. With an international team (below), Blumenschine continues excavations here. Sediments offer him clues to the rise and fall of lakes and springs. Bone fragments gnawed by teeth or gouged by tools help him reconstruct ancient relationships among predators, scavengers, and prey.

ever explained these satisfactorily," he says.

Berger first got the notion that an eagle killed the Taung child when he saw one swoop down and fly off with a monkey. He found the eagle's nest and, working with Ron Clarke, documented that the bones left on the ground resembled the animal fossils found alongside the Taung child. He also found the skull of a young baboon with puncture wounds similar to the child's.

"The world was a cruel place for early hominids," says Berger. "They not only had to watch every bush they passed by, every rock they turned over, and every tree they walked under," he says, "but now we know they also had to keep one eye on the sky."

But around 2.5 million years ago life irrevocably changed for hominids. In Ethiopia I see the reason why.

"THESE ARE THE OLDEST KNOWN stone tools," says Yonas Beyene, director of archaeology and anthropology for the Ethiopian Ministry of Information and Culture in Addis Ababa. "They were made 2.6 million years ago," he adds as he presents a box holding sharp-edged flakes and fist-size choppers from a site called Gona.

Thousands of such tools have been excavated by a team led by Sileshi Semaw and Jack Harris of Rutgers University. "Making them was a simple process," Beyene tells me. "The hominids picked up one stone and broke it with another. That gave them a sharp cutting edge that could pass through an elephant's hide—something hominid teeth could not do."

Tools were used not only to cut meat into edible pieces; they could also smash bones in order to expose the fat-rich marrow and dig roots and tubers. Scavenging for carnivore leftovers, especially the marrow and brains, became a hominid way of life.

The use of tools to cut meat probably coincided with the increased size of the hominid brain. "If you found an abandoned leopard kill, you could get your day's nutrition in half an hour," says Robert Blumenschine, a paleoanthropologist at Rutgers University. "But you have to be smart to be a good scavenger."

And as early hominids grew smarter, they developed better tools. Imagination may have been born when our ancestors developed the ability to think about a tool they needed and then create it, says Kathy Schick, a stone-tool specialist at Indiana University. "Experimenting with different shapes of tools represents the earliest form of science," she adds.

With the increase in brain size, the hominid body began to change in other ways. "Each gram of brain tissue needs twenty-two and a half times as much energy to keep it alive as muscle tissue at rest," explains Leslie Aiello, an anthropologist at University College London. "If you want to grow a big brain, you have to shrink some of your other expensive organs, such as your kidney, liver, or gut."

While scientists are beginning to understand the biological ramifications of creating and using stone tools, they remain uncertain about which hominid invented them. Many believe that australopithecines were capable of fashioning simple tools, but others see toolmaking as a sign that *Homo,* with its larger brain and greater intelligence, had evolved. However, no *Homo* fossils as old as the Gona tools have been found.

Paleoanthropologists have gotten close though. A mandible recently found at Uraha in Malawi by Tim Bromage of Hunter College and Friedemann Schrenk of the Hessisches Landesmuseum in Darmstadt, Germany, may be our oldest *Homo* specimen. "We think this was a young adult who lived about 2.4 million years ago," says Schrenk in his office, holding up the two pieces of a brown jawbone that retains its blackened teeth.

Others question the accuracy of the age Schrenk and Bromage propose for the Malawi mandible. Andrew Hill of Yale University tells me that a 2.4-million-year-old skull fragment from Lake Baringo in Kenya represents the oldest *Homo.* Meanwhile, Donald Johanson and Bill Kimbel recently announced finding the upper jawbone of an unidentified *Homo* at Hadar and have dated the fragment to at least 2.3 million years ago.

The fossil record for early *Homo,* however, remains scanty, and specialists argue over how many species existed. For many years the earliest *Homo* fossils were all categorized as *Homo habilis,* after fossils discovered at Olduvai Gorge by Louis and Mary Leakey in the 1960s. New family trees have recently been drawn that break a second species, *Homo rudolfensis,* off from *habilis.* Fossils of the more advanced *Homo erectus,* which scientists previously thought emerged around 1.5 million years ago, have been dated as early as 1.8 million years ago, indicating that *erectus*

Members of the family

In the fossil vault of Kenya's National Museums, Richard Leakey displays four of his extraordinary finds, all from the Lake Turkana region. The skull of a robust australopithecine, far left, though part of the hominid family tree, rests on a separate branch. Clustered together from center to right, *Homo* skulls spanning 300,000 years are all more closely related to modern humans.

lived at the same time as *habilis* and *rudolfensis*. And some scientists now want to create a separate *erectus* branch, known as *Homo ergaster*. Thus, the early *Homo* family tree is starting to look as bushy as the australopithecine one.

Specialists do agree that the tree gained an important branch with the emergence of *Homo erectus*. Its body was the culmination of all the anatomical changes the early hominids had made over the previous two million years. Taller, leaner, and able to move quickly across the savanna, *erectus* was poised to spread out from Africa to the far-flung ends of Eurasia. But though its body design closely resembled ours, its mind is still a mystery.

"It was the velociraptor of its day," is how Alan Walker, one of the leading authorities on *erectus*, sees this new hominid. "If you could look one in the eyes, you wouldn't want to.

It might appear to be human, but you wouldn't connect. You'd be prey."

Walker's opinion inflames other scientists, who argue that even chimpanzees show human emotions like compassion. "Anyone who has spent just a few seconds with a chimp or a gorilla knows that these primates relate closely to us," says Meave Leakey. "Certainly *erectus*, with a brain capacity greater than living apes', would relate even more closely to us."

Paleoanthropologists—like philosophers—will no doubt continue to argue about the basic nature of our ancestors. If I could look into the eyes of an early hominid, what would I see? A velociraptor's chilling glare or the glimmerings of compassion and caring? I choose compassion, but I cannot ignore the inhumanity I see reported daily on the news. Perhaps in some ways we are still walking the road to becoming human.

Striking questions

A broken skull from Swartkrans, South Africa, appears before an image of the lightning that frequently strikes the high veld. Some researchers suggest that this hominid gathered smoldering wood from lightning-ignited fires and used it to cook meat. Others argue that the charred animal bones found at the site are simply traces of naturally occurring flames. The evidence is equivocal and energetically debated by scientists, who continue searching for the origins of distinctively human life.   □

Time is running out for
the world's largest cat.
Reeling from the double
punch of poachers and
habitat loss, only a few

Siberian Tigers

hundred survive in the
wild. While zoos work
to maintain the animal's
genetic diversity, Russian
and American scientists
are pooling their efforts
in the fight to save this
magnificent creature
from extinction.

By MAURICE HORNOCKER
Photographs by MARC MORITSCH

Running for fun, a young adult tiger named Koucher grabs at Niurka, a female, at a study site in eastern Russia. This game of chase is more than play. It sharpens hunting skills and helps the pair bond and live harmoniously. Later, the tigers nap.

The world of Koucher and Niurka is a three-acre enclosure in the village of Gayvoron, 190 miles from the Sikhote-Alin Biosphere Reserve, one of four set up in this region to protect wildlife

A RESEARCH
PROJECT
SUPPORTED
IN PART
BY YOUR
SOCIETY

habitat. Russian scientists work in concert with the Siberian Tiger Project of the Hornocker Wildlife Institute, a project that Howard Quigley and I began in 1989 at the University of Idaho.

It is not known exactly how many Siberian tigers roam free; like most large, secretive carnivores, they are hard to count. The latest estimate is around 430. Our work is aimed at increasing that number through better protection of the animals.

The story of Koucher and Niurka is sadly not uncommon. They were among two sets of cubs orphaned when their mothers were killed by poachers, according to Victor Yudin, a vertebrate biologist at the Russian Academy of Sciences in Vladivostok. The cubs were given to Yudin for care. But two cubs were too malnourished to survive.

The winters of 1992, '93, and '94 were hard on Siberian tigers. Many were killed for their coats and body parts. The demise of the Soviet Union led to the opening of Russia's borders. That made it easier for illegal traders to cross into China and Southeast Asia, where tiger bones and organs are prized for their supposed potency as medicines and aphrodisiacs.

MAURICE HORNOCKER is director of the Hornocker Wildlife Institute. For information write: P.O. Box 3246, University of Idaho, Moscow, Idaho 83843. MARC MORITSCH is photographer for the institute.

A gaping grimace allows Koucher to take in scents in his territory. Known as flehmen behavior, this contortion increases access to the vomeronasal organ, which is located above the palate and covered with sensory cells. Flehmen behavior is normally exhibited at sites where other cats have marked their territory by spraying their scent.

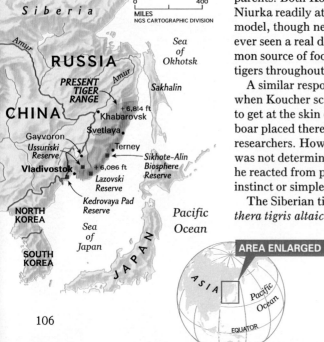

Obeying a primal urge, Koucher pounces on a plastic foam model of a deer. The model is mounted on a wire and pulled through the enclosure by a researcher who stands out of sight. For added realism, the model was scented with deer urine. The experiment was devised to study the predatory instinct among tigers who as youngsters had not received any training in hunting by their parents. Both Koucher and Niurka readily attacked the model, though neither had ever seen a real deer, a common source of food for all tigers throughout Asia.

A similar response came when Koucher scaled a tree to get at the skin of a wild boar placed there by the researchers. However, it was not determined whether he reacted from predatory instinct or simple curiosity.

The Siberian tiger, *Panthera tigris altaica*, at one time populated a great swath of Asia that stretched from Siberia south through China into North and South Korea. The Siberian tiger is in trouble largely because of its great commercial value. A single tiger can bring in $15,000, more than most local people make in years.

The upswing in poaching during the early 1990s coincided with a decrease in government funding of conservation efforts and an increase in forestry, mining, and road construction that further shrank the Siberian tigers' natural habitat. Loss of habitat and overhunting has also reduced the populations of the tigers' chief prey: elk, wild boar, and deer.

Our efforts and those of several other organizations are beginning to pay off. Reserve acreage in the region has been increased, antipoaching squads have been strengthened, and the courts are treating convicted poachers more harshly.

Perched outside the den where he was born, a male cub named Globus surveys the enclosure. He and a brother were born to Koucher and Niurka. (The parents themselves may have been siblings; matings between close relatives may occur in the wild and don't necessarily produce genetically inferior offspring.) Niurka abandoned the cubs, which is not uncommon among first-time tiger mothers in captivity. Despite great efforts to save Globus's brother, he died of malnutrition.

Though malnourished himself, Globus survived, thanks to the care of Victor Yudin (lower left), who cuddled and bottle-fed the cub for months. By seven months Globus weighed in at 129 pounds and loved to roughhouse with Yudin (below). Full-grown, Globus could weigh as much as 800 pounds.

In October 1996 we took Globus to the Minnesota Zoo near Minneapolis. At maturity he will add a welcome infusion of new genetic material to the captive-management program.

Since Globus's birth, his parents have produced three more cubs. Because they are dependent on humans, the parents and cubs will have to stay in captivity. But our ultimate goal remains to work with Yudin to provide insights into tiger behavior and to develop conservation initiatives to secure a future for the tigers in the wild. ☐

Learn more about Siberian tigers at http://www.nationalgeographic.com on the World Wide Web or on CompuServe at GO NATIONAL GEOGRAPHIC.

By JOEL L. SWERDLOW
NATIONAL GEOGRAPHIC SENIOR WRITER
Photographs by BOB SACHA

Seventy stories below
daylight, "sandhogs"
install air ducts in a new
artery for New York
City's water. City Tunnel
No. 3 will add 60 miles
to a multilayered sub-
terranean network that
slakes the city's thirst,
transports its people,
and channels its light,
heat, and voices.

New York
Under

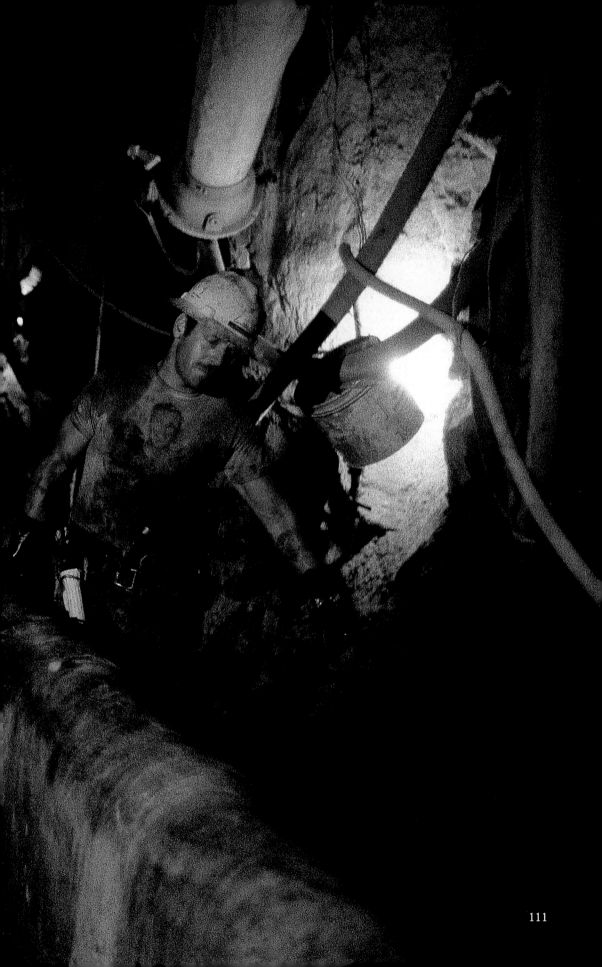

Maestro of rush hour, James Graseck strikes a final note as a train pulls into the Herald Square Station. The violinist performs in Lincoln Center, Carnegie Hall, and the subway. "I'm not playing for strangers," he says. "I'm playing for a bulk of humanity. They're like extended family.

Subway Song

I become part of their commute." Each day 3.5 million
people ride the subway, along whose 230-mile route
the city grew. "The symbol of New York may be the skyscraper," writes transit historian Clifton Hood. "Yet, without the subway, the skyscraper would be an empty shell."

113

"**E**VERYONE GETS SCARED on his first sewer dive," Jeff Kwami, a 12-year veteran says. "It's not a normal place to be." My plastic bodysuit crinkles as I climb down a manhole in Queens. Two pairs of gloves cover my hands. Over my shoulder is an emergency tank filled with a ten-minute supply of air. As part of safety training, I have learned about methane, hydrogen sulfide, and other potentially lethal or explosive gases formed by decomposing organic waste.

Like most people, I have lingered at an open manhole, thankful I did not have to go down into that dark, confined space. Despite this fear, I have been fascinated. Looking beneath a city street is like peeking under your own skin—the terrain upon which your well-being depends is so close, yet so full of secrets.

Now I am visiting the underworld that keeps New York City alive. More than 32 million miles of utility lines range in depth from just below the street to more than 80 stories down. No one turns on a light, cooks a meal, or warms an apartment without tapping into these lifelines. Maps of them look like the circuitry of a rocket. Color-coding helps. Red is gas. Orange is electric. Yellow is steam. Pink is telephone. Black is television cable.

I am climbing through this subterranean rainbow to reach its deepest and least accessible layers: water mains and sewers, represented by blue and brown on the map. Then I will sample the more familiar transportation facilities, 22 underwater tunnels and 443 miles of underground subway tracks. Although a feeling in my gut says, "Don't do this," I am excited to leave the surface.

BOB SACHA is a freelance photographer who lives 14 floors aboveground in Manhattan.

After only seconds in the manhole—in reality, a subterranean brick chimney—I realize how completely this underground has its own rules, which visitors break at their own risk.

"Go slowly," says Jeff, who stands on a platform about 30 feet below the surface, clinging to the safety line harnessed to my back. I am 40 feet down, standing on a two-foot-wide concrete ledge. In front of me is a swift river of human waste—what sewer workers call "nasties." The six-foot-diameter tunnel is filled only halfway, because most people in this residential neighborhood are still at work. At 7 a.m. and after 5 p.m. sewer tunnels are often too full to visit. When Jeff or his colleagues search for leaks or blockages, they usually descend late at night, when people are sleeping and toilet flow is low.

Above me I hear the thunder of cars crossing manhole covers. If I close my eyes and ignore the smell, the rush of water sounds idyllic. "What happens if you fall in and you're not attached to a rope?" I ask Jeff. "If you don't pull yourself out at the next few manholes," he answers with a shrug, "you'd be taken downstream a few miles to the processing plant." There I'd be trapped underwater and drown.

Processing the sewage, mostly removing harmful bacteria, yields 310 tons of sludge—also called biosolids—each day. Seventy percent is formed into pellets and sold as organic fertilizer. One-quarter is shipped to Texas and spread on semiarid grassland. The rest goes to a landfill. The sludge contains hundreds of tons of the toxic chemicals, metals, and other industrial wastes that seep—or are dumped—into the sewer system each year. The pollutants unaffected by these procedures end up in New York's waterways.

Behind me as I stand at the edge of the flowing sewage are large brick troughs. Everything down here is moist and slippery, so I inch my feet around to look beyond these troughs into an empty storm-runoff tunnel. This alone makes the trip down worthwhile because it shows me how things work.

This sewer, like 70 percent of those in New York and many in older American cities, is also a collection facility for storm runoff. After a downpour yielding a half inch of rain or more, the sewage will flow over the floor on which I am standing, spill into the troughs, and exit through the storm-runoff tunnel directly into Flushing Bay. Thus, New York regularly pollutes surrounding waterways with raw, unprocessed sewage. One possible solution to this problem is underground tanks that hold overflow until it can be processed. But such tanks are expensive, and few neighborhoods want them nearby.

"See any alligators?" Jeff asks, as we head back up. He is joking about one of New York's most enduring myths—that baby alligators get flushed into the sewers and grow to monstrous proportions.

I tell Jeff about one confirmed sighting reported in the *New York Times* in 1935. A seven-footer was hauled out of a sewer onto a snowbank in upper Manhattan. No one knows where it came from.

Jeff laughs, clearly not believing me. I thank him, forgetting to say that his friendly professionalism made my anxiety disappear.

THIS SAME KIND of reassurance eases my next descent. I ride with "sandhogs," the nickname for tunnel workers, down a construction shaft into a new water tunnel that will link the city to its water source in the Catskill Mountains more than a hundred miles away. The most expensive public works project in the city's history, City Tunnel No. 3 is designed to bring one billion gallons of fresh water into New York City each day.

We are headed 670 feet below Queens. The elevator, lit with an exposed bulb, travels slowly and quivers. Its sides are wire grill. At about 150 feet down daylight disappears and the air gets cooler. After two minutes we pass the point, 503 feet from the surface, where a worker was crushed in 1993 when a 16-ton winch fell down the shaft.

Over the underworld • NYNEX technicians crouch at the brink of a three-story-deep manhole. Below their feet, 208,000 telephone lines thread into the looming World Trade Center. "It's a puzzle," says Eddie Melendez, at bottom. Some 465,000 manholes punctuate New York streets, narrow passages into the city's roots.

Soon there will be nearly 700 feet between me and the street. I look up into darkness and down into deeper blackness, wondering whether fears will creep in. Fear of falling and fear of being trapped underground both seem justified. What most worries me, however, is that when the elevator stops about 20 feet from the bottom of the shaft, I will have to climb down a slippery metal ladder wearing knee-high, loosely fitting boots. If I fall, landing on the rocks below, I will have to be hoisted out. Being so far underground bothers me far less than the possibility of this embarrassment.

The shaft itself is an open geology textbook. Its walls are primarily schist, gneiss, and granite, formed between 450 and 550 million years ago during the Ordovician and Cambrian periods. About 200 million years ago the rock mass split into parts of Europe, Africa, and North America. Before the split the chunk that became New York folded and refolded at least seven times, leaving fault lines. More faulting may have come from earthquakes caused by the retreat of glaciers beginning about 100,000 years ago. All these faults involve only one plate and are therefore less worrisome than those in California, where two plates grind against each other. An earthquake of about 5 on the Richter scale rattles New York roughly once a century, the last in 1884. An earthquake of 5.5—unlikely, but not impossible—could make small buildings collapse. At 7, skyscrapers, built to endure movement caused by wind, would lose their facades and utilities.

I reach the bottom without incident. Looking back up the shaft, I see only black haze and realize how stupid I am to be standing here. If someone drops a tool or kicks over a rock, it could do a lot more than ruin my day.

Safety lies in the dust and smoke of the 23-foot-wide, dimly lit tunnel. This smoke comes from 500 pounds of dynamite that the sandhogs have just detonated at the end, or "heading," of the tunnel. A hundred detonators, timed to explode thousandths of a second apart, have loosened about 12 feet of rock. The sandhogs will haul this muck up the shaft, moving the tunnel forward 12 feet a day. When the tunnel is big enough, they will lower a 640-ton, bug-shaped tunnel-boring machine that chews rock at 90 to 100 feet a day.

The tunnel, *(Continued on page 123)*

Caught in the light • Awakened in a crawl space in Grand Central Terminal, a homeless man known only as Lamine greets Metro-North police officer Bryan Henry. Soon after, Lamine stopped living in the terminal. Fifty people lived in the station's tunnels in 1989. Today none do. Efforts citywide have reduced the underground homeless from 5,500 to 1,000. Bob Kalinski (below) left this Amtrak tunnel last April. "Living down there, you either grow or you die," he says. "I've decided to grow."

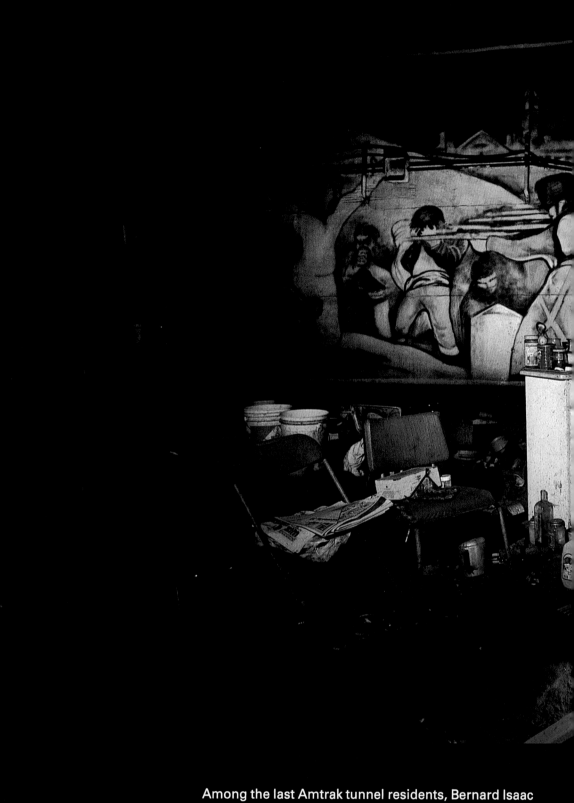

Lord of the Tunnel

Among the last Amtrak tunnel residents, Bernard Isaac lights a cigarette as he waits for water to boil. During his 11 years beneath Riverside Park, Isaac built a communal kitchen 30 yards from the tracks, where graffiti artists painted the mural of an execution, copying a classic

work of Goya. Isaac left last June, but only after the railroad ordered him out. "I miss the tunnel," says Isaac, who moved into an apartment in Harlem. "Now I have sirens, car sounds. I really wanted to stay behind after they got everyone out, just to have some peace."

SUBWAYS
Most subway tunnels were built within 50 feet of the surface. Workers excavated block-long trenches in which they built rectangular structures of steel beams and concrete. These boxes were buried and utilities replaced above.

Parking garage

Foundation

Cap

PILES
Groups of piles, such as these steel beams, are driven into bedrock to carry structural weight. Once enough piles are in place to support a column, they are capped with concrete.

Subway entrance

Water pipes

Token booth

Turnstiles

Abandoned utility pipes

Telecommunications and electrical cables

Water main

Gas pipe

Sewer pipe

Steam pipe

Steam vault

Electrical vault

Gas vault

Storm drain

UTILITIES
Telephone lines share ducts with police and fire alarm systems. High-voltage electrical cables are in separate ducts. Steam, gas, and water move in valved pipes.

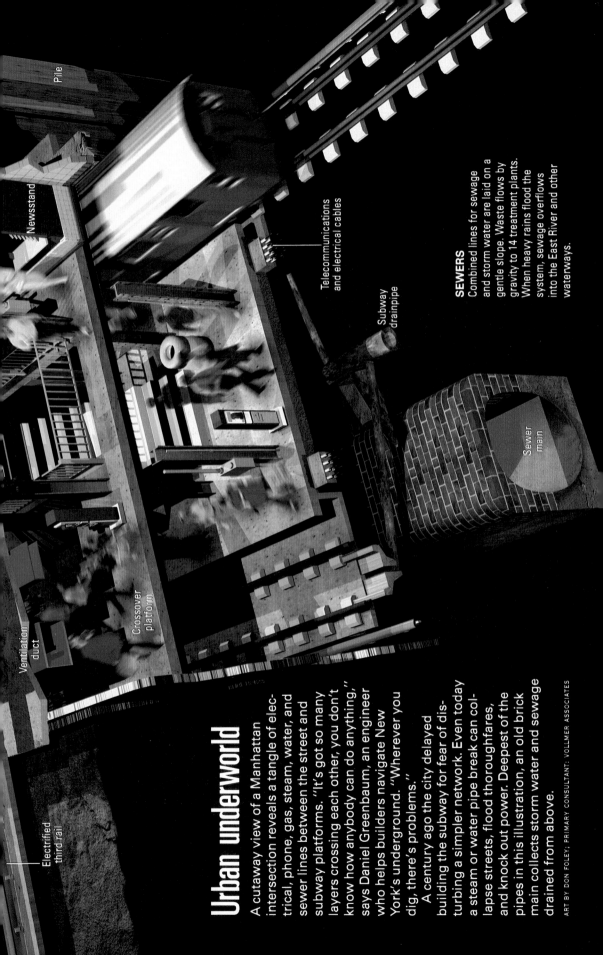

Urban underworld

A cutaway view of a Manhattan intersection reveals a tangle of electrical, phone, gas, steam, water, and sewer lines between the street and subway platforms. "It's got so many layers crossing each other, you don't know how anybody can do anything," says Daniel Greenbaum, an engineer who helps builders navigate New York's underground. "Wherever you dig, there's problems."

A century ago the city delayed building the subway for fear of disturbing the simpler network. Even today a steam or water pipe break can collapse streets, flood thoroughfares, and knock out power. Deepest of the pipes in this illustration, an old brick main collects storm water and sewage drained from above.

Electrified third rail

Ventilation duct

Crossover platform

Newsstand

Pile

Telecommunications and electrical cables

Subway drainpipe

Sewer main

SEWERS

Combined lines for sewage and storm water are laid on a gentle slope. Waste flows by gravity to 14 treatment plants. When heavy rains flood the system, sewage overflows into the East River and other waterways.

ART BY DON FOLEY; PRIMARY CONSULTANT: VOLLMER ASSOCIATES

(Continued from page 116) which extends about 175 feet, is the stage for a primitive battle between man and rock. Across its walls and roof the sandhogs have bolted a metal grid to keep loose chunks from falling on them. Where the dynamite exploded, they jab the walls and ceiling with 20-pound iron poles, trying to knock down whatever is loose. I touch the rock and am shocked by how sharp it is. Shortly before I came down, falling rock had sliced open a sandhog's fingers. From being in the aboveground changing room known as the "hog house," I know that the bodies of most sandhogs are spackled with scars.

"Why do this work?" I ask Brian Gallagher, who at age 32 has been a sandhog for 16 years. Brian—nearly killed in 1993 by the falling winch that killed one of his friends—is the son of a sandhog. Such traditions are common; some families have worked on New York's underground since the first subway at the turn of the century. I expect to hear about pride, about being where no one has ever been before, about helping to build the city's future.

"It's the money," Brian says. "I can make a lot more down here than anywhere else." An experienced tunnel worker earns more than $100,000 a year.

Another sandhog standing nearby tells me, "We are the invaders. This has been here for millions of years, and we're not meant to be here."

I do feel like an invader. As I remove my goggles to examine water dripping from the tunnel wall, one of the sandhogs tells me to keep them on. "Everything here can kill you," he says. He is not being macho; he is stating a fact that has bred gruff camaraderie. "Twelve go down and twelve come up," a foreman says. The governing ethos seems to be: Don't think about being scared, but do everything possible to protect yourself.

Sandhogs who die on the job are usually killed in avoidable accidents. Human biology can contribute. In the near darkness of a tunnel the pineal gland assumes it is night and produces the hormone melatonin, which is associated with fatigue and inattention.

Sharp drop • Sandhogs guide a 16-ton front-end loader into the same tunnel where a miner was killed last September when he fell off a boring machine. Twenty-four have died since work on this water tunnel began in 1970. The city's first aqueduct was hailed as a miracle in 1842 and was finally shut down in the 1950s. Cavers exploring the old tunnel (below) illuminate stalactites formed as water drips through mortar.

As WE RIDE UP, I look at the sandhogs' faces, searching for more than fatigue. Chances of dying while working on this water tunnel are far greater than a New York City police officer's chances of being killed while on duty. The third water tunnel, now 18 miles long, has cost more than a man a mile. At that rate, 42 more sandhogs will die before it is done.

The remaining construction will take the tunnel under the East River and into lower Manhattan. Investment in such infrastructure seems improbable in today's antitax atmosphere, but over the next decade taxpayers will spend even more on underground transportation projects. To begin exploring these facilities, I walk the bottom level of the 63rd Street Tunnel, which runs more than one and a half miles from Queens to midtown Manhattan.

While the tunnel's upper level has carried subway trains since opening in 1989, the bottom level has never been used. It is an empty

Nerve surgery • A NYNEX technician splices lines in the city's 32-million-mile phone system. Wires were first laid underground after overhead lines snapped in the Great Blizzard of 1888.

concrete corridor. Above is the East River; behind and in front of me blackness stretches. A red growth, some kind of bacteria, creeps through cracks in the floor. It is the only bright color I have ever seen that looks unhealthy.

By now I have learned why I like being underground. To be cut off from the routines and concerns of surface life feels strangely safe. You disappear into yourself down here.

The Long Island Rail Road, which manages this lower level, plans to extend the existing tunnel by two miles, connecting it to Grand Central Terminal on Manhattan's East Side. Pamela Burford, the 35-year-old transit planner who supervises the tunnel project for the railroad, and Richard Mitchell, a 64-year-old construction engineer at the Metropolitan Transit Authority who helped design the tunnel, walk through it with me. He describes how workers scoured and blasted the bottom of the river to create a pocket, then filled 380-foot-long steel tubes with water and sank them. Divers guided the tubes into place. After pumping them full of pressurized air and covering them with ten feet of rock to keep them from floating up, workers climbed inside and bolted them together. The greatest problem, Mitchell says, came from currents, which kept moving the river bottom before the tubes could be secured.

Our flashlights reveal puddles of water, some ankle deep, from groundwater seeping into the tunnel. We pass beneath Roosevelt Island, which lies between Long Island and Manhattan. Near the door to an emergency exit huge letters proclaim, "SANE: The Dead Live!" Sane was the nom de plume of a graffiti writer who left his mark throughout New York's subways. Authorities never convicted him, and rumors about him persist, even though he died in 1991.

The tunnel ends several hundred feet into Manhattan. Above us, accessible by 15 stories of emergency stairs, is Second Avenue. Pam stares at the raw, exposed rock of the heading—a 20-foot-high circle of grayish black, with symmetrical grooves left by a tunnel-boring machine. "I've never been here before," she says out loud, not really talking to me. "I've been to the other end of the tunnel, but I've never come all the way."

She steps forward and lays one hand, palm flat, on the rock, staring forward—as though looking into it, through the tunnel that does not yet exist. Nearly two miles of rock lie

Rooted in rock

Much of Manhattan rests on clay, sand, gravel, and boulders deposited by Pleistocene glaciers. Sandhogs have dug 22 underwater transportation tunnels through this debris and bedrock. Below, they have blasted two water tunnels through gneiss and schist. They are boring a third to serve as a backup for a system carrying 1.5 billion gallons a day.

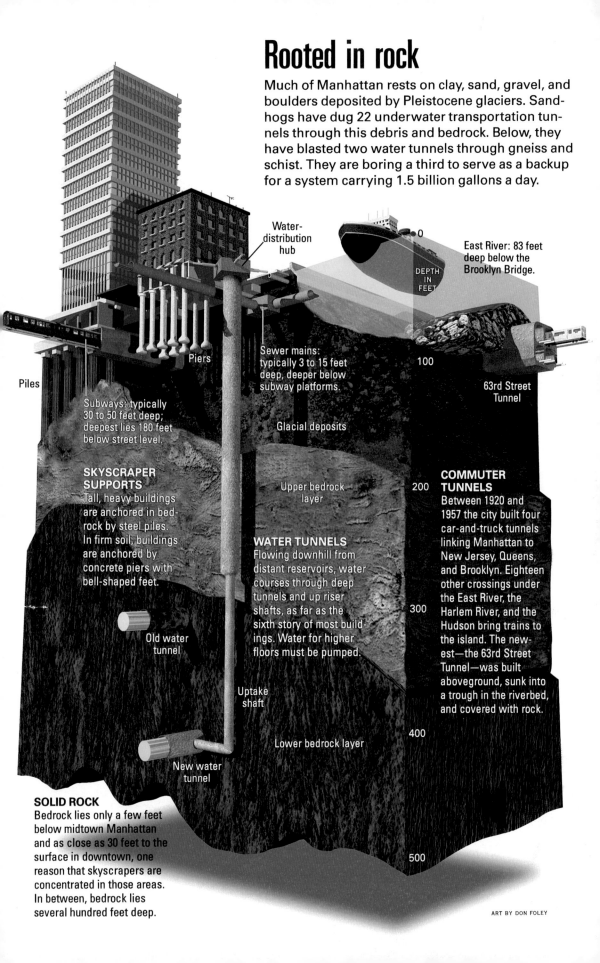

Water-distribution hub

East River: 83 feet deep below the Brooklyn Bridge.

0

DEPTH IN FEET

Piers

Sewer mains: typically 3 to 15 feet deep, deeper below subway platforms.

100

63rd Street Tunnel

Piles

Subways: typically 30 to 50 feet deep; deepest lies 180 feet below street level.

Glacial deposits

SKYSCRAPER SUPPORTS
Tall, heavy buildings are anchored in bedrock by steel piles. In firm soil, buildings are anchored by concrete piers with bell-shaped feet.

Upper bedrock layer

200

WATER TUNNELS
Flowing downhill from distant reservoirs, water courses through deep tunnels and up riser shafts, as far as the sixth story of most buildings. Water for higher floors must be pumped.

Old water tunnel

300

COMMUTER TUNNELS
Between 1920 and 1957 the city built four car-and-truck tunnels linking Manhattan to New Jersey, Queens, and Brooklyn. Eighteen other crossings under the East River, the Harlem River, and the Hudson bring trains to the island. The newest—the 63rd Street Tunnel—was built aboveground, sunk into a trough in the riverbed, and covered with rock.

Uptake shaft

Lower bedrock layer

400

New water tunnel

SOLID ROCK
Bedrock lies only a few feet below midtown Manhattan and as close as 30 feet to the surface in downtown, one reason that skyscrapers are concentrated in those areas. In between, bedrock lies several hundred feet deep.

500

ART BY DON FOLEY

between her and Grand Central Terminal.

"When this tunnel is done, my four-year-old daughter will be in college and I'll be ready to retire," she says. She kneels, picks up a piece of rock, and puts it in her pocket.

THE GRAND CENTRAL connection, scheduled to open in 2010, will cut commuting time for an estimated 40,000 Long Islanders who work on the East Side. Today they take the train into Penn Station on the West Side and double back by foot, bus, taxicab, or subway.

Such commuter links are increasingly important to megacities like New York. Despite computer and fax connections that make it easier to work at home, the number of workers filling Manhattan high-rises is climbing. But without high-speed transportation, downtown regions atrophy, which is why cities as diverse as Beijing and Los Angeles are building new underground rail systems.

Stuart Lerner, a 35-year-old structural engineer with Vollmer Associates, walks me through the Times Square subway complex, the nation's busiest. It serves 400,000 people each workday. Some 57,000—about the number that fill Yankee Stadium—pack in during its busiest hour alone. Such crowds, a 1996 study by the Regional Plan Association concludes, are of "inhuman proportions." Walking through this station during rush hour, I feel more claustrophobic than in the other tunnels I have visited. People press on all sides, pushing, making it impossible to change directions. I feel trapped.

One Flight Down • A bassist descends into the Village Vanguard, a famed jazz club wedged into a basement. "Once you walk down those stairs, you are in a womb," says owner Lorraine Gordon. Ten thousand lights glow along the arches of the Oyster Bar, beneath the main concourse of Grand Central Terminal.

Stu's job is to help finish a 35-million-dollar station expansion. Included will be the first elevators in Times Square's main station. As we stand in one of the many passageways, Stu points to a low concrete ceiling. "This is where an elevator will go," he says. "It will require going up through the street." He unrolls a large map—a spaghetti bowl of gas, electric, telephone, cable, steam, water, and sewer lines. "They're all between us and the street," he explains. "We've got to dig through them."

"How can you understand this map?" I say. "Everything crosses everything else."

Stu smiles. "It's actually more complicated than the map," he says. "Manhattan is the most dense underground site in the country. Once you start to dig, you never know what you're going to hit. Often people don't take things out. They abandon things in place, throwing new on top of old, so later you have to figure out what's operative and what's not."

We go up to the street, where a water main broke a day earlier: Nearly 70 percent of the city's pipes are at least 50 years old, and a break occurs virtually every day. Workers use shovels to dig around the concrete tubes that hold utility lines. Some tubes hang by wires from boards spread across the hole, which looks like a drawerful of silverware turned upside down. "There's plenty of room to add more," Stu says. "Most new stuff is fiber optics for communication."

Stu tries one last time to get me to understand the map. "How'd you like to thread a needle through all of this?" he asks. "That's what we'll do when we build the elevator, and we'll have to do it without cutting anything."

He will be operating on the city's underbelly, its most vulnerable spot. Broken utility pipes have killed or injured dozens of people since 1990. The number of lives disrupted can be enormous. In 1989 a steam pipe break killed three people and sent pieces of street soaring 18 stories high. Such vulnerability is the prime reason that utilities restrict access to their maps. To know the underground grid would be a terrorist's dream.

A DIFFERENT KIND of vulnerability worries me as I return to the subway. Crime, encouraged by darkness and decrepitude, was common when I rode the New York subway regularly in the late 1970s. Bloodstains on station platforms were not unusual.

New York toughness is still here—when a man was shot recently during a robbery attempt, delaying the train until medics arrived, angry passengers swore at him for making them late. But I am amazed by how much safer the subway feels these days. Most cars and stations are reasonably clean and well lit. New subway-car paint, from which other paint can be easily washed, helped eliminate most graffiti. Nonetheless, "scratchiti," writing or drawings etched by vandals, cover virtually every subway car window.

Three junior high school students show me how they paint graffiti on subway tunnels. Ignoring large rats, which they call "tunnel rabbits," they enter the tracks from stations. They risk arrest, getting hit by a train, and touching a 600-volt rail. Their handiwork is a

Empty of passengers as it changes direction, a local
slips by a special tour of the 1904 City Hall Station,
designed as a showplace for the first subway but closed
when trains grew too long. After half a century it will
reopen next year as a museum. Between 1982 and 1996

Turnaround

the New York City Transit Authority spent 13 billion
dollars to reverse decades of decay in the subway. Air-
conditioning returned, trains traveled ten times as far
between breakdowns, and graffiti disappeared. Stricter
law enforcement has cut felonies by two-thirds.

blight, but sometimes someone leaves words worth reading. In one tunnel—used only by Amtrak trains—I find: "We all live in a tunnel of darkness. Yet few meet fearlessly the demons they refuse to see. Tunnel of darkness. Inner light."

Police arrest graffiti writers as part of a new policy that has reduced felonies on the subway by two-thirds since 1990: Catch people for the small crimes so they cannot commit large ones. Police used to ignore turnstile jumpers, people who enter the subway system without paying their fare. Now officers look for them. In 1995, 5 percent of those arrested carried weapons.

Despite crime reduction, the subway still conveys a sense that civilization is about to lose its grip, that chaos is just around the corner. Veteran riders share their survival wisdom. Don't sit near doors, because someone could rob you as the door is closing. Keep alert to everyone around you, but don't look anyone in the eye, because someone might take it the wrong way.

Staying aware of people while not looking them in the eye is a skill quickly mastered. A bad smell moves through a subway car, radiating from a man who seems otherwise normal. No one looks at him or exchanges glances. Being together under such circumstances is, for the system's 3.5 million daily riders, a meditation on aloneness. At one station I sit in the middle of a three-seat wooden bench. A young man sits to my right. Sheet music covers his lap. He hums as he reads the music, his fingers moving as though playing a piano. To my left a woman sits down, opens a compact, looks in the mirror, and brushes on eyeliner. Then, perhaps subconsciously, she begins to hum the same song as he. I sit between them, silent and invisible.

WE NEVER ACKNOWLEDGE IT, but the three of us need each other. The rule under New York is the same as the rule above: Make sure other people are always nearby. It is 10:30 a.m. The train I am on empties, and suddenly I am alone, sitting beneath one of New York's toughest neighborhoods. The car stops at the next station, and its doors open. Who will get in? Will they see me as a good target? Only later do I remember that when a car empties, you should get off—even if it is not your stop—and wait until you can ride with other people.

Numbers increase safety but guarantee nothing. The *New York Daily News* carries a letter from Josiah H. Brown, special assistant to the president at the New School for Social Research. He describes sitting in a subway car. A man starts to punch him. "His fists struck without warning, throwing me off the seat," Brown writes. "My repeated shouts of, 'Someone help me! Please!' were ignored by some 20 fellow passengers. . . . Scrambling quite possibly for my life, I glimpsed them sitting, inert, impassive. No one responded, no one moved, no one even offered a kind word when it was over."

The New York Police Department keeps no statistics on the indifference of bystanders. "What would you do if you saw someone being assaulted?" I ask my fellow riders. Most ignore me. Most of those who answer say they would do nothing. "Would you sit while it was happening?" elicits shrugs and blank looks. Fear of guns and knives is understandable, but this could be some lower ring of Dante's Inferno, a place where people who could help you do nothing.

Unlike those trapped in Dante's hell, subway passengers have a choice. I want to stand up and shout, "You don't have to sit there in fear. If enough of you are willing to care, your numbers give you strength. There's no need to ride day after day indifferent to each other."

But, like a New Yorker, I sit silently, hidden behind an expressionless face. I too need the true hero down here, someone to shatter the indifference, reminding everyone that human contact is possible.

During one morning rush hour, on a platform beneath Grand Central, my hero comes in an unexpected package: a 42-year-old man, slender, with bouncy straight hair, wearing a ruffled white shirt and tuxedo pants. His name is James Graseck. As he plays the violin, people slow down, look at each other, and smile. With each piece he offers a quick commentary. "Vivaldi is describing the icicles forming," says Jim, who then calls Paganini "the Mick Jagger of the 19th century."

A man hums his favorite opera, hoping Jim will know it. One woman sets down her briefcase and spends 30 minutes listening and talking with other people. "I didn't hear enough, but I have to be at work," another man says. Many people are regulars. "I count on his being here," one woman confesses.

It may be my imagination, but women seem more moved by Jim's music than men are. When he takes a break, I ask him about this, and he admits that 14 years ago, when he felt a great urge to play and pulled out his violin on a Manhattan street corner, his future wife was among the people who stopped to listen.

Shortly after that Jim started to play in the subway. He has stayed down here because of the excellent acoustics and the crowds. Many of the approximately 3,000 people who hear him every hour hire him for private parties and recitals; more than 2,000 paid up to $25 each in 1993 to hear him play in Carnegie Hall. Jim, who has a master's degree from the Juilliard School and once received rave reviews for a solo concert in Lincoln Center, sees how I am looking at him. He stops playing and says to me, "It's weird, isn't it?" I know what he means, weird that someone with his talent plays in the subway, and I nod. "Well," he says, "this is New York." A woman overhears our conversation. "He's a rose in mud," she tells me.

Riding the subway until late afternoon leaves me eager to go back to sunlight and fresh air. I look for Jim to say good-bye, and I hear his notes dancing along the platform. People turn, drifting in his direction. On a nearby bench, a woman has tears in her eyes. Sunlight and fresh air can wait. I sit and listen. ☐

Learn more about subterranean New York next month at http://www.nationalgeographic.com on the World Wide Web or on CompuServe at GO NATIONAL GEOGRAPHIC.

Inbound jumbos • Elephants march through the Queens-Midtown Tunnel, closed so the circus could enter Manhattan. Weekdays, 3.4 million people commute to the central business district. Two-thirds use the tunnels, descending as many as 13 stories, then ascending into towers that draw life from the world below.

UPI, CORBIS-BETTMANN

■ FROM THE GEOGRAPHIC ARCHIVES

Weehawken, Here We Come

Taking the newest route to New Jersey, cannon-carrying Army trucks rumbled though the Lincoln Tunnel in midtown Manhattan during opening ceremonies in December 1937. In the tunnel's first year of operation, 1,790,647 motorists paid 50 cents each way to take the 8,000-foot shortcut under the Hudson River. Today some 20 million vehicles make the trip each year, the toll has quadrupled—and all cannon are expressly forbidden. The most explosive things in the tunnel now are traffic-ignited tempers. "We'd prefer people leave those at home," said one Port Authority official.

This photograph was never published in the magazine.

Will you cross the Serengeti any time soon? Probably not.

You're more concerned with day-to-day adventures.

Like commuting. Shopping. Or scenic country drives.

So we designed the Bravada® to perform best where you drive most.

On-road. We gave it the kind of suspension to give you

the kind of ride and handling you wouldn't expect from an SUV.

To give you the confidence to tame just about any road. **Bravada**

WARREN FAIDLEY

■ 1997 EDUCATIONAL VIDEOS AND VIDEODISCS CATALOG
Tools for Teachers

A BOLT OF LIGHTNING can generate 200,000 amps of electricity and be five times as hot as the surface of the sun (right). Yet students may be shocked to discover that many of those struck by lightning survive to tell their tales. *When Lightning Strikes* is one of 51 videos recently released specifically for use in the classroom. The full line of National Geographic videos—over 400 titles—is featured in the 1997 Educational Videos and Videodiscs Catalog, available by calling 1-800-368-2728.

The Society's classroom products combine award-winning filmmaking with content famed for accuracy and balance. Correlated to school curricula and the national geography standards, each video comes with a teacher's guide.

A new line called GeoKits was inspired by teachers' suggestions. Each kit comes complete with maps, posters, and student handouts.

From *Insects* to *Steal Away: The Harriet Tubman Story*, the videos make learning vivid for students from pre-K through high school.

■ EXPLORER, FEB. 16, 7 P.M. ET
Under the Spreading *Dipteryx* Tree

CROAKING LOVE SONGS on a tropical night, a male *Hyla* frog (right) adds his voice to the chorus around Panama's Barro Colorado Island, protected under the stewardship of the Smithsonian Tropical Research Institute. Scientists from all over come to this field station to untangle the mysteries of a tropical forest.

EXPLORER's "Panama Wild" takes viewers on a scientific odyssey from the forest canopy—called the last frontier on earth—to the mud below.

JOHN BROWN, OXFORD SCIENTIFIC FILMS

Central to life are the towering hundred-foot *Dipteryx* trees, venerable giants whose fruit and foliage support hundreds of other species.

■ PROGRAM GUIDE

National Geographic Specials
  NBC. See local listings.
National Geographic EXPLORER
  TBS. Sundays, 7 p.m. ET.
National Geographic Videos and Kids Videos Call 1-800-627-5162.

West Indian Manatee *(Trichechus manatus)* **Size:** Head and body length, 3 - 4 m **Weight:** 500 - 1,000 kg **Habitat:** Coastal waters, estuaries and rivers from southeastern USA to northeastern Brazil **Surviving number:** Estimated at less than 3,000 in Florida; unknown elsewhere   Photographed by Joel Sartore

WILDLIFE AS CANON SEES IT

A manatee finds its winter refuge in the warmth of Florida's freshwater springs. In shallow waters, the manatee walks along the bottom on its front flippers, but in deep water it cruises about in slow motion, surfacing every few minutes to breathe. Also called sea cows, these docile herbivores consume huge amounts of aquatic plants daily, making them invaluable as natural cleaners of clogged waterways. In Florida, many manatees become victims of motorboat propellers. Habitat loss and hunting, which still occurs in some areas of its range, also contribute to the manatee's endangered status. As a global corporation committed to social and environmental concerns, we join in worldwide efforts to promote greater awareness of endangered species for the benefit of future generations.

Retinal Camera
Versatile and easy to operate, Canon's CR5-45NM non-mydriatic retinal camera allows small pupil photography without requiring pupillary dilation, greatly facilitating procedures related to ophthalmology and medical diagnosis.

*Earth*Almanac

Freshwater Marshes Treat
Sewage With a Natural Flush

HARNESS FRAGILE WETLANDS, so vulnerable to pollution, to treat sewage? It seems a contradiction, but since 1986 Arcata, California, has been using freshwater marshes, home of this American bittern and other wildlife, as part of the municipal sewage system. Before then, partially treated waste had sometimes flowed into Humboldt Bay.

First the city had to restore the marshes, which had been smothered by a landfill, by planting bulrushes and other plants. Now as the effluent is pumped through as many as six marshes, "nutrients in the wastewater fertilize the plants," says botany professor Robert Rasmussen of Humboldt State University. "As the marsh matures, there are more plants to pull more nutrients out of the water. After full treatment the wastewater that goes into Humboldt Bay is almost clean enough to drink," he says. The project has inspired several others nearby.

J. MARK HIGLEY

IT'S THE NEW ROUGH AND RUGGED FULL-SIZE SUV* THAT'S AS COMFORTABLE AS ALL-GET-OUT. FORD EXPEDITION. IT'LL GET YOU THERE LIKE NOTHING ELSE.

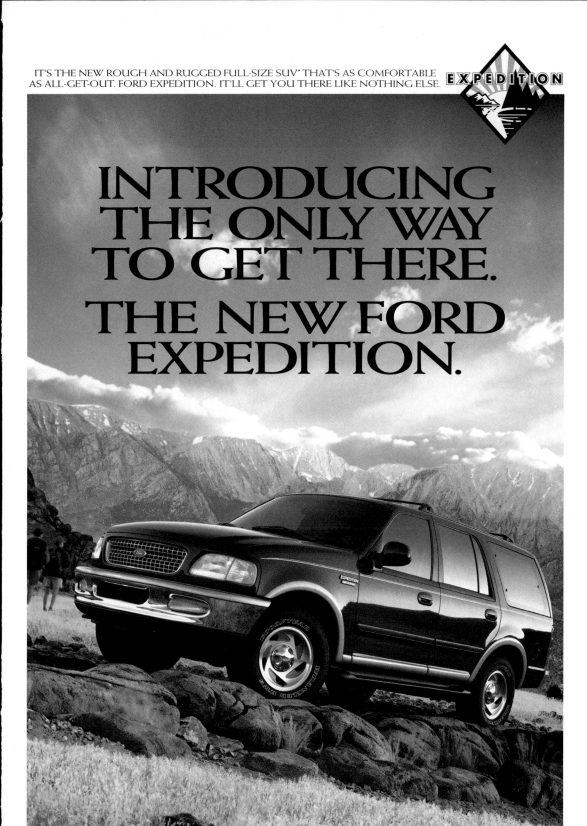

INTRODUCING THE ONLY WAY TO GET THERE.
THE NEW FORD EXPEDITION.

*Sport utility vehicle. **Always wear your safety belt.

Best-In-Class Towing: Properly equipped 4x2 tows four tons. **Best-In-Class Passenger Room:** XLT models seat up to nine. Fits in a Standard-Size Garage. Standard Dual Air Bags.** For information: 1-800-434-4040 or www.ford.com

Crafty Spider Mimics Moths' Scent

NAMED FOR the South American bola snare, bolas spiders excel at capturing moths. Females spin a silken thread with a sticky droplet at the end. When a moth appears, the spider swings the thread until it sticks. Then the huntress cocoons her prey—here a bristly cutworm moth—to eat later. But the weapon is short-ranged. To bring moths closer, the spider uses deception. She produces chemicals similar to pheromones used by females of several moth species to attract mates. When male moths show up, they find only a fatal attraction.

SPIDER, *MASTOPHORA HUTCHINSONI*; MOTH, *LACINIPOLIA RENIGERA*; DARLYNE A. MURAWSKI

This "Tree" Is Wired for Positive Feedback

WIRELESS TECHNOLOGY is on a roll. Every day more than 31,000 customers join the U.S. cellular phone system, now totaling 38 million people. But there's an aesthetic price: antenna towers, usually 150 feet tall, are needed to link the devices. Many zoning boards disapprove of such blights.

What if the antennas looked like trees? Four companies—ARCNET of New Jersey, the Larson Company of Arizona, Valmont Industries of Nebraska, and AT&T—are jointly creating camouflaged antennas, like this 125-foot white pine model in Atlanta. Covered with epoxy-resin bark, the steel pole conceals antennas inside branches. Average cost: a thousand dollars a foot. The firms also plan to offer royal palm and saguaro cactus designs.

JOHN RATCLIFFE, ARCNET

Bugging Horns to Track a Few Surviving Rhinos

A RARE SUBSPECIES, the northern white rhino numbers only about 30 in the wild. All are guarded in Zaire's Garamba National Park, where they remain vulnerable to poachers seeking meat

KES & FRASER SMITH AND JANE MOORE

and horns. Vigilance failed last year when a male and a pregnant female were killed.

Another male rhino, Bonne Année, was among several fitted with a radio transmitter in his horn (above). "The devices help us to direct antipoaching patrols," says zoologist Kes Smith. —JOHN L. ELIOT

KENNETH GARRETT

■ EARLY HOMINIDS
Taking a Taste of Prehistory

MUNCHING ON TERMITES to sample the hominid diet didn't bug Rick Gore (above, at right) while he was in South Africa with paleoanthropologist Lee Berger. It was part of the job. "I was also interested to learn how important high fat food—meat and marrow—was in human evolution. We might not have grown big brains without it. That seems odd in today's 'low fat' culture."

Insect-eating was one more lesson in human diversity, Rick says, "which you learn as soon as you start going overseas on assignment." In the course of his 23-year GEOGRAPHIC career, the senior assistant editor has dined on warthog, wildebeest, hippo, a camel's milk potion that made him sick for days, "and intestines of every kind," he recalls. "My rule of thumb is always to take one bite, except for unfamiliar mushrooms—and slugs."

You really do have to draw the line somewhere.

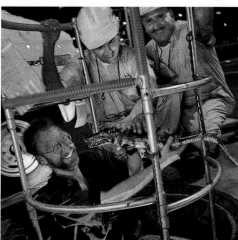

TIM WILLIS

■ UNDER NEW YORK
An Underworldly Experience

HOW DO YOU PHOTOGRAPH DARKNESS? "With very little light," laughs Bob Sacha, who faced just that problem shooting subterranean New York City. "It took a long time to get that underground feeling in the pictures," he admits. When Bob, a longtime Manhattan resident, would tell friends about his experiences covering this story, they would always ask the same thing: "Are there really alligators in the sewers?" So, in a manhole leading under the World Trade Center (left), he revealed the long-secret location of the city's most famous reptiles. Where are they? "On the shelf in any toy store," Bob says. "If you want to find alligators in New York's sewers, you're just going to have to bring them down there yourself."

NATIONAL GEOGRAPHIC (ISSN 0027-9358) IS PUBLISHED MONTHLY BY THE NATIONAL GEOGRAPHIC SOCIETY, 1145 17TH ST. N.W., WASHINGTON, D.C. 20036-4688. $25.00 A YEAR, $5.00 A COPY. PERIODICALS POSTAGE PAID AT WASHINGTON, D.C., AND ELSEWHERE. POSTMASTER: SEND ADDRESS CHANGES TO NATIONAL GEOGRAPHIC, P.O. BOX 2174, WASHINGTON, D.C. 20013.

Wider Is Better.